Anxiety Disorders

Con... ...e
Panic Attacks, Phobia & Anxiety.
Plus Information On Medication.

- Julie Stevenson -

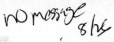

On Hold

For

Patron name: **Eaton, Nicole**

Item barcode: 1030002963879

Title: Anxiety disorders : concise blueprint to overcome panic attacks, phobia & anxiety plus information on medication / Julie Stevenson.

Author: Stevenson, Julie.

Call number: RC531 .S73 2008

Pickup location: CMC Steamboat Springs C726

Pull date: Thu Nov 03 2016

Patron Phone: 9708712040

Patron email: njeaton@mail.coloradomtn.edu

Anxiety Disorders

Concise Blueprint To Overcome Panic Attacks, Phobia & Anxiety. Plus Information On Medication.

Discover what can put you at risk of developing anxiety and what can be done to prevent it from happening again. Find out why doctors are so keen to prescribe medication.

- Julie Stevenson -

Cranendonck Coaching
Maarheeze, The Netherlands

3

Author Online!

For updates and more resources
visit Julie Stevenson's Web Site at

www.regain-control.com

ISBN 978-90-79397-02-0

For Further Help

Though Julie is glad to receive feedback, she cannot provide private consulting. For further help, please consult a health professional.

1.0

Publisher: Cranendonck Coaching,
              Maarheeze, The Netherlands

Contents

Chapter 1 - Introduction 7

Chapter 2 – So What Is Anxiety? 11

Stress Or Anxiety 14

Chapter 3 – Types of Anxiety Disorders 18

General Anxiety Disorder 18

Panic Disorder 19

Agoraphobia 20

Phobias 21

Obsessive Compulsive Disorder 23

Post Traumatic Stress Disorder 25

Summary 26

Chapter 4 - Diagnosis 29

Self Tests 30

Chapter 5 - What Causes Anxiety Disorders? 32

Long Term, Predisposing Causes 32

Chemical Imbalances - Biological 37

Short-Term, Triggering Causes 38

Maintaining Causes 38

Chapter 6 - Treatment 41

Medication for Anxiety 41

Therapy 49

Use Affirmations 64

Choosing The Right Mental Health Professional 65

Tips For A Support Person 66

Chapter 7 - Natural Supplements 70

Chapter 8 – Nutrition and Anxiety 73

Caffeine 73

Nicotine 75

Sugar 76

Stressful Eating Habits 77

Changes You Can Make 78

Chapter 9 - Talking To Yourself 79

The Worrier 79

The Self Critic 79

The Victim 80

The Perfectionist 80

Stress building Personality Test 83

Chapter 10 - Coping with Attacks 85

Deflate the Danger 86

Deep Relaxation 92

Visualization 93

Chapter 11 - Exercise, Exercise, Exercise... 98

Choosing An Exercise program 99

Getting Your Program Started. 100

Using Exercise To Help Reduce Anxiety 102

Overcoming Excuses For Not Exercising 102

Chapter 12 - Use the Tools You Have 105

Reference 106

Chapter 1 - Introduction

A few years back, I started experiencing something I never had before. Out of nowhere I started getting chest pains and feeling as if I was going to pass out. I was dizzy and breaking out in a cold sweat and I could not catch my breath. I was crying hysterically because I was positive I was having a heart attack. I even convinced myself that my arm was going numb. After nearly a week of this happening nearly every night I finally had enough and made my husband (who was my fiancé at the time) take me to the hospital at 9 p.m. at night. Never mind that he had to work early the next morning and I had to prepare for my brothers wedding which was two days away.

While at the hospital, I started to feel better, but not better enough that I wanted to leave. When I was finally brought into a room to be examines, I was so tired I just wanted to sleep but there were tests to be done. From 11 p.m. until nearly 1:30 am I was poked, prodded and pushed until they finally determined that nothing was wrong with me or my heart. My blood pressure was up and I was offered a nitro patch which I refused. By this point I had realized that I was not dying and I was certainly not having a heart attack. The doctor told me I had a "panic attack" or an "anxiety attack" and wrote me a prescription for Xanax then sent me on my weary way.

A few weeks later the same panic happened again. My chest hurt, my pulse was racing and once again we trekked to the emergency room and I was convinced this was it I was having a heart attack. Again, I was told I simply had a panic attack and it was recommended I follow up with my doctor this time. The third time it happened, my husband had enough and refused to go wait with me in the emergency room. My mother came with me this time and somehow managed to convince me to leave and take a Xanax at home. She even made me breath into a paper bag to help me catch my breath. While I admit I felt like a fool doing this, it really did help me.

I could not understand where all the sudden this "panic" was coming from, but I hated it every time it happened. I felt alone and scared whenever this uncontrollable feeling of something bad happening to me came over me. I felt like I had no control over it. Pretty soon, it was starting to affect my daily life. I would lock myself in the bathrooms at work because I was afraid something was happening to me and I did not want any of my co workers to see me. I could not even go out to have something as simple as an eyebrow waxing done because I was afraid something would happen on the table. I even freaked out on the day of my bridal shower. I had such a headache that day, that I had convinced myself I was having an aneurysm. I got worse if I heard a story about someone dying very suddenly and began not sleeping at night because I was afraid I would not wake up the next morning. In fact I spend many a nights crying myself to sleep because I had convinced myself that I would not wake up. Factor in the headaches I was having, and the constant stream of chest pains, I was a walking mess. It was certainly not a healthy way of life for me and to make it worse I kept it all bottled up inside, but I was slowly coming apart at the seams.

I finally caved in and called my doctor. Or rather I was almost forced to. My then fiancés told me that unless I take some steps to find out what was going on with me, he was not going to go through with the wedding. It was probably not the best way to get me to get help, but it made me get help. I went in for my appointment and I told him how I was scared of a brain aneurysm, a heart attack, a blood clot, and a stroke. I fully expected my doctor to laugh or at the very least roll his eyes at my dramatics. He didn't though in fact my doctor sent me for every test imaginable to rule out all of the above and to give me a piece of mind. I had and MRI and an MRA, which incidentally sent me

8

into even more of a panic because of the closed space you, are in. I was also sent in for more blood work and an echocardiogram to rule out blood clots. Everything came back normal. My doctor had hoped that with proof of a clean bill of health, my anxiety and panic would stop, but it didn't. In fact it seem to take a turn for the worse and after my fourth appointment, he gently suggested that I meet with a therapist to get to the root of my problem.

Tip:

Don't hesitate to find another doctor if you feel your current doctor doesn't understand your specific needs or is uneducated about anxiety disorders. Don't let him or her intimidate you or discount how you are feeling.

It took me a while to keep my appointment with the therapist. I have had bad experiences in the past with them and wasn't looking forward to seeing yet another one, but the problem was becoming so severe that I could barely make it out of the house. I knew I had to do something plus it was starting to affect my relationships with other people. No one could understand what I was feeling, and some didn't even try to. I was sick of being isolated from everyone so I finally met with the doctor and after a few weeks, I finally had an answer about what was going on with me. I was diagnosed with a panic disorder, agoraphobia and general anxiety disorder.

Finally I had an answer to what was wrong, but I didn't quiet understand it. I asked my doctor and was told that a panic disorder was an anxiety disorder. Anxiety? I never thought of myself as having anxiety. I mean yes, I worry a lot and maybe a little more than the next person but I didn't realize it was having such an impact on my life. I was at the beginning to my road to recovery and I wanted to get to the end as fast as possible. Before

I could start though I needed to get to the bottom of what this all was and why I was suddenly out of no where suffering from it.

Suggestions for doctor visits:

- Ask to be seen first or last, for shorter times waiting in the examination room.

- Take several measures of blood pressure throughout the visit, in the knowledge that it will go down as you get used to being there.

- Have a glass of water available.

- Ask that a staff member to check in on you while you wait for the doctor.

- Have a support person with you.

Chapter 2 - So What Is Anxiety?

You would be surprised at how many people confuse anxiety with fear. They are two different things. Fear is usually directed at someone, something or a specific situation. You can have a fear of certain things like bugs or animals. I for one am deadly afraid of spiders. I scream it I see a spider web because I know that means a spider is lurking somewhere but I do not associate any sort of danger with spiders.

I know people who are afraid of flying (again, I am but that stems from my general anxiety disorder) and some people who are scared of heights. While being on a plane can bring on an anxiety attack, it has less to do with flying.

Anxiety is more internal. You may feel like you are losing control or as some people say "you are jumping out of your skin". You could be anxious about going to the doctors to find out test results, or you could be anxious about getting a review on an article you had written or something you had done. Usually with anxiety there is more of a physical reaction along with an emotional reaction. You may find you can't sleep while you are worrying or thinking about the event coming up that is making you anxious. Have you ever found yourself not being able to sleep the night before a big presentation, or not being able to eat the day of an interview for a job you really want? Those are all symptoms of anxiety. Granted, it is not the type of anxiety that will send you into some sort of attack, but it is anxiety just the same. Anxiety is a part of life and it is normal to experience some form of anxiety at some point or another. In fact, I would be worried if you didn't experience some form of anxiety at one point or another.

Children even experience some form of anxiety at some point or another. They are anxious about starting school, or camp , etc.

Now Anxiety and anxiety disorders are two different things. An anxiety disorder is a more intense feeling of anxiety (for example, panic attacks) that lasts for quite some time. Normally your anxiety will go away after the event or situation is over and done with. When you have an anxiety disorder, you may have the anxiety for months on end and the disorders could lead to phobias or fears that affect your life. This is exactly what had happened to me. I was so anxious of having the same experience as my father that I was never fully comfortable away from my loved ones. Even now, when I have my GAD and my attacks under control, I still find myself having flare-ups if my husband and daughter are away from me for too long.

Another distinction between anxiety and anxiety disorder is the fact that the latter can lead to phobias that interfere with your life.

There are several anxiety disorders. There is General Anxiety Disorder, Panic Disorder, Obsessive-Compulsive disorder, post-traumatic stress disorder, agoraphobia and social phobia to name a few.

I found out that anxiety disorders are the number one mental health problem among American women and the second only to alcohol and drug abuse among men. Roughly 15 percent of the US population, or nearly 40 million people, have suffered from panic attacks, phobias, or other anxiety disorders in the past year.

Even more disturbing is the fact that nearly a quarter of the adult population will suffer from an anxiety attack at some time during their life! Yet only a small proportion of these people receive treatment.

Stages in Anxiety:

<u>Mild</u>

Tension of day-to-day living; you have a better ability to interpret or become aware of something through your senses (you have an alert perceptual field); a mild stage of anxiety can motivate learning. Example: anxiety felt when missing the bus.

<u>Moderate</u>

Focus is on immediate concerns: perceptual field is narrowed; you show selective inattention. Example: anxiety felt when taking an exam.

<u>Severe</u>

Focus is on specific detail; perceptual field is greatly reduced. Example: anxiety felt when witnessing a car accident.

<u>Panic</u>

You experience a sense of awe, dread, and/or terror; you lose control; there is a disorganization of the personality. Example: anxiety felt when experiencing an earthquake and being unable to cope.

Before focusing on the different types of anxiety orders I'll first take a closer look at the differences between stress and anxiety.

Stress Or Anxiety

Contrary to popular belief, there is a difference between stress and anxiety. Stress comes from the pressures we feel in life, as we are pushed by work or any other task that puts undue pressure on our minds and body, adrenaline is released, extended stay of the hormone causes depression, a rise in the blood pressure and other negative changes and effects.

One of these negative effects is anxiety. With anxiety, fear overcomes all emotions accompanied by worry and apprehension, making a person a recluse and a bagful of jitters. Other symptoms are chest pains, dizziness, and shortness of breath and panic attacks.

Stress is caused by an existing stress-causing factor or stressor. Anxiety is stress that continues after that stressor is gone. Stress can come from any situation or thought that makes you feel frustrated, angry, nervous, or even anxious. What is stressful to one person is not necessarily stressful to another.

Anxiety is a feeling of apprehension or fear and is almost always accompanied by feelings of impending doom. The source of this uneasiness is not always known or recognized, which can add to the distress you feel.

Stress is the way our bodies and minds react to something which upsets our normal balance in life; an example of stress is the response we feel when we are frightened or threatened. During stressful events our adrenal glands release adrenaline, a hormone which activates our body's defense mechanisms causing our hearts to pound, blood pressure to rise, muscles to tense, and the pupils of our eyes to dilate.

A principal signal of increased stress is an escalation in your pulse rate; however, a normal pulse rate doesn't necessarily mean you are not stressed. Constant aches and pains, palpitations, anxiety, chronic fatigue, crying, over or under-eating, frequent infections, and a decrease in your sexual desire are signs you may notice which suggest you may be under stress.

Of course, every time we are under stress, we do not react to such an extreme and we are not always under such great duress or fear every time we are confronted with a stressful situation.

Some people are more susceptible than others to stress; for some, even ordinary daily decisions seem insurmountable. Deciding what to have for dinner or what to buy at the store, is a seemingly, monumental dilemma for them. On the other hand, there are those people, who seem to thrive under stress by becoming highly productive being driven by the force of pressure.

Research shows women with children have higher levels of stress related hormones in their blood than women without children. Does this mean women without children don't experience stress? Absolutely not!

It means that women without children may not experience stress as often or to the same degree which women with children do. This means for women with children, it's important to schedule time for yourself; you will be in a better frame of mind to help your children and meet the daily challenge of being a parent, once your stress level is reduced.

Anxiety, on the other hand, is a feeling of unease. Everybody experiences it when faced with a stressful situation, for example before an exam or an interview, or during a worrying time such as illness. It is normal to feel anxious when facing something difficult or dangerous and mild anxiety can be a positive and useful experience.

However, for many people, anxiety interferes with normal life. Excessive anxiety is often associated with other psychiatric conditions, such as depression. Anxiety is considered abnormal when it is prolonged or severe, it happens in the absence of a stressful event, or it is interfering with everyday activities such as going to work.

The physical symptoms of anxiety are caused by the brain sending messages to parts of the body to prepare for the "fight or flight" response. The heart, lungs and other parts of the body work faster. The brain also releases stress hormones, including adrenaline. Common indicators of excessive anxiety include:

• Diarrhea

• Dry mouth

• Rapid heartbeat or palpitations

• Insomnia

• Irritability or anger

• Inability to concentrate

• Fear of being "crazy"

• Feeling unreal and not in control of your actions which is called depersonalization

Anxiety can be brought on in many ways. Obviously, the presence of stress in your life can make you have anxious thoughts. Many people who suffer from anxiety disorders occupy their minds with excessive worry. This can be worry about anything from health matters to job problems to world issues.

Certain drugs, both recreational and medicinal, can also lead to symptoms of anxiety because of either side effects or withdrawal from the drug. Such drugs include caffeine, alcohol, nicotine, cold remedies, and decongestants, bronchodilators for asthma, tricyclic antidepressants, cocaine, amphetamines, diet pills, ADHD medications, and thyroid medications.

A poor diet can also contribute to stress or anxiety -- for example, low levels of vitamin B12. Performance anxiety is related to specific situations, like taking a test or making a presentation in public. Post-traumatic stress disorder (PTSD) is a stress disorder that develops after a traumatic event like war, physical or sexual assault, or a natural disaster.

In very rare cases, a tumor of the adrenal gland (pheochromocytoma) may be the cause of anxiety. This happens because of an overproduction of hormones responsible for the feelings and symptoms of anxiety.

Chapter 3 - Types of Anxiety Disorders

General Anxiety Disorder

If you have been diagnosed with GAD, it means that you have chronic anxiety that lasts for at least six months. Chances are you might have no idea what it is you are so worried about but everyday you are filled with worry and tension. The key is you don't have as many of the other physical symptoms that are associated with other panic disorders.

Most doctors state that, to diagnose someone with GAD, your anxiety and worry focuses on two or more stressful life situations like your health or your relationships for most of the time during a six-month period. Essentially you have no control over these worries.

Besides worrying, people with GAD usually experience at least three of these symptoms though not every single day:

• Restlessness

• Getting tired easily

• Hard time concentrating

• Irritability

• Muscle tension

• Insomnia

Besides these main symptoms, some suffers of GAD also complain of frequent headaches, difficulty swallowing, trembling, and sometimes hot flashers.

If you suffer from GAD, you are not alone. Statistics show that nearly 6.8 million adults suffer from GAD. It can start at any age. Children and teens have been diagnosed also with GAD because they worry about school performance or sports performances. Chances are if you have GAD, you can still function in your everyday life.

Panic Disorder

One of the unfortunate outcomes from suffering from excessive stress and apprehension is a physical reaction of your body to the situation. It's like your body is telling you that you need to rest for a moment. Except when you're having a panic attack, it's anything but restful.

As I said earlier, I would start getting cheat pains, heart palpitations and fears of going crazy usually out of the blue. I was a classic example of someone suffering from Panic Disorder. Other symptoms that come with the panic attacks associated with panic disorders are

• Dizziness and faintness

• Trembling

• Feeling of Choking

• Sweating

• Stomach pains, nausea

• Feeling of unreality

• Tingling in hands and feet

- Hot and cold flasher

- Fears of going crazy

- Fears of dying.

Now most of these are common responses for our "flight or fight" instinct. The biggest difference is that usually a certain danger will trigger these feelings in us, while a panic attack will come out of nowhere. Panic attacks can be scary because the symptoms can be similar to a heart attack or at least what we think is a heart attack would be like. Most people who experience a panic attack for the first time will wind up seeking medical advice.

Agoraphobia

This is perhaps the most common anxiety disorder. It is estimated that 1 out of every 20 people suffer from some form of Agoraphobia. Alcoholism is the only other disorder in America that affects more people than agoraphobia. The textbook definition of agoraphobia means fear of open spaces but it is really the fear of panic attacks. This means that most people with agoraphobia avoid places where they might not be able to leave easily if they have a panic attack and avoid possible embarrassment. Most of the time not only is the panic attack scary but what other people think as well.

My agoraphobia kept me out of many public places when I was at my lowest. I lost count of how many times I had almost finished my grocery shopping only to feel the all too familiar heart pounding and pulse racing sensations and I would bolt from the store and arrive back home empty handed but shaking from fear. I learned that one of the most common features about agoraphobia is anxiety about being far away from home or a safe person. This was true for me. I hated to be away from my husband and felt like something was wrong if I wasn't with him. I still to this day get nervous if I'm away from him or my daughter. Agoraphobia usually comes with a panic disorder. A panic disorder is when you have no idea why a panic attack happens, but once you become aware that these attacks can tend to happen more when you are alone or in small spaces you will find that you don't want to be alone.

Not every person who has a panic disorder will develop agoraphobia, nor will every 2 people have the same severity of it. However it is known that it can be caused by a combination of heredity and environment. When I say heredity I mean that it can be a learned trait. In fact children whose parents are agoraphobic have a higher risk of developing it themselves because it is what they learned. I remember wondering when in the world did I develop a panic disorder. In nearly 28 years, I have never had one before and it wasn't until my diagnosis that I dove into learning all I could about this one disorder. Usual the causes are heredity, chemical imbalances and personal stress. One of the most effective treatments for panic attacks is to begin to realize the signs of an oncoming panic attack and being able to ride the attack out. We'll talk more about that later.

Phobias

This category involves a strong, irrational fear and avoidance of an object or situation. The person knows the fear is irrational, yet the anxiety remains. Phobic disorders differ from generalized anxiety disorders and panic disorders because there is a specific stimulus or situation that elicits a strong fear response. A person suffering from a phobia of spiders might feel so frightened by a spider that he or she would try to jump out of a speeding car to get away from one.

People with phobias have especially powerful imaginations, so they vividly anticipate terrifying consequences from encountering such feared objects as knives, bridges, blood, enclosed places, certain animals or situations. These individuals generally recognize that their fears are excessive and unreasonable but are generally unable to control their anxiety.

Social Phobia

This is another common anxiety disorder and it involves the fear of embarrassment in public situations. Now you may be thinking that everyone at one point or another suffers from some sort of nervousness when it comes to being in a social situation or a performance situation. I myself get nervous before big gatherings and tend to get a little crazy any time I was due on stage. he difference is these feeling passed. If you suffer from social phobia, your feelings are a little deeper. You worry is that you will be judged on everything you say and do. If you do something wrong you will be looked at as anxious, weak or even crazy. The most common fear of social phobia is speaking in public and it can affect performers, speakers and anyone whose job requires them to make presentations. Other social phobias are

• Fear of blushing in public

• Fear of being watched at work

• Fear of using public toilets

• Fear of crowds

• Fear of taking examinations

Because social phobias are so common, some doctors will only give an actual diagnosis of social phobia only if your avoidance is interfering with work, social activities or relationships. Also, if you suffer from panic attacks from the sheer thought of doing something in public, you are probably suffering from social phobia.

The biggest difference between panic attacks and panic attacks brought on by social phobia is that social phobia panic attacks stem from your fear of being humiliated rather than feeling trapped or fearing for your life. Also these attacks to not come out of the blue but rather when you are faced with a certain type of social situation. Usually medications can be prescribed for social phobia. People have benefited from taking medication such as Paxil to treat their phobia but most people benefit more from social skills training. They relearn basic social skills like smiling and making eye contact along with active listening.

Specific Phobia

This category involves a strong, irrational fear and avoidance of an object or situation. The person knows the fear is irrational, yet the anxiety remains. Phobic disorders differ from generalized anxiety disorders and panic disorders because there is a specific stimulus or situation that elicits a strong fear response. A person suffering from a phobia of spiders might feel so frightened by a spider that he or she would try to jump out of a speeding car to get away from one.

People with phobias have especially powerful imaginations, so they vividly anticipate terrifying results from facing such feared objects as knives, bridges, blood, enclosed places, certain animals or situations. These individuals recognize that their fears are excessive and unreasonable but are generally unable to control their anxiety.

Obsessive Compulsive Disorder

I'm sure all of us know at least one person who we might have joked at one point or another that they are obsessive compulsive. It might be the neat freak that we know or the person who keeps hand sanitizer at their desk. But obsessive compulsive is a real disease. Let's break it down to what the words obsessive compulsive even mean.

Obsessive are recurring ideas, thoughts and images that may seem senseless but still manage to enter your mind. You realize that they are irrational but you still are constantly thinking about them. You may spend hours or days thinking about them even though you don not want to.

Compulsions are rituals that you perform to dispel the anxiety brought up by the obsessions. If you constantly obsess about if you locked your door or not, you will probably find yourself checking your locks constantly if you have a compulsion about it.

The thing about obsessive compulsions is that you know they are unreasonable yet you still find the need to do it. The most common compulsions are washing, checking and counting. Washers are obsessed with avoiding contamination and may spend hours a day showering and washing their hands. They may avoid doorknobs, handshakes or touching anything that might have come into contact with something toxic. Women tend to be a lot more of the washer types while men are the checkers.

A checker will check to see if their door is closed and locked constantly because of an obsession of being rob, they are constantly checking their stoves to make sure no burners are left on due to obsessions about a fire happening to them. While it is normal to have some obsessions about this, I for one am always checking to make sure I locked my doors but it is mainly because I can be more absent minded than anything else.

Lastly you have the counting obsession which is when a person must count up to a certain number or repeat a certain word of times to get rid of anxiety. Or they must count to a certain number to brush their teeth, their hair or even wash their hands. Other symptoms of it can be having to stick to personal rules of how to walk, and eat. Some people have to cut their food into the right amount of pieces before they can eat it.

A very early onset of OCD is early childhood but most of the time it is missed because no one thinks that OCD is a possibility this young. Usually the most effective way to manage OCD is medication and behavioral therapy.

Post Traumatic Stress Disorder

I think this is the most talked about anxiety disorder. You constantly hear about people suffering from Post Traumatic Stress. For those of you who might not know exactly what it is, it is a disorder that can occur in anyone regardless of age, after they have experienced a severe trauma that is outside their threshold to handle. Many soldiers suffer from post traumatic stress because of what they may see overseas. It has been reported that some survivors of the 9-11 attacks on the World Trade Center and the Pentagon suffer from PTSD as well as survivors of Hurricane Katrina. PTSD can affect anyone who has been involved in any of the following: a car crash, a plane crash, rape attack or any other violent crime against themselves or their family. To be diagnosed with PTSD you usually have most if not all the following symptoms for at least a month.

• Repetitive, Distressing thoughts about the trauma

• Nightmares about the experience

• Reliving the experience through flashbacks

- Avoidance of thoughts or feelings from the experience

- Avoidance of activities that are associated with the experience. For example some people who developed PTSD after a serious car accident have a sudden phobia about driving or even getting into a car

- Being out of touch with your feelings

- Feelings of detachment from others

- Losing interest in things you used to enjoy

- Increased anxiety

Sufferers of PTSD often state they are depressed as well and sometimes lash out at those closest to them. Again therapy and medication is the best treatment for this disorder.

Summary

The information provided in this chapter might be overwhelming. That's why I'll provide you with a summary of major anxiety Disorders.

General Anxiety Disorder

Definition: Anxiety focused on various life events or activities

Symptoms: Restlessness, fatigue, difficulty in concentrating, irritability, muscle tension, sleep problems

Panic Disorder

Definition: Discrete episodes of intense anxiety that begin abruptly and reach a peak within about 10 minutes

Symptoms: Palpitations, sweating, trembling, shortness of breath, sensation of choking, chest pain, nausea, dizziness, fear of losing control, fear of dying, sense of altered reality.

Agoraphobia

Definition: Acute anxiety in crowds; fear of being alone; fear in any physical setting from which the individual may have trouble escaping

Symptoms: Intense feelings of anxiety or fear of losing control that results in either refraining from going out or avoiding situations that may cause anxiety

Phobia

Definition: Persistent, excessive, or unreasonable fear of a specific object or situation (examples: elevators, airplanes, dogs, spiders, injections, tunnels)

Symptoms: Fears that interfere markedly with life activities

Obsessive-Compulsive Disorder

Definition: Happening of recurrent thoughts, images, or impulses that are intrusive and inappropriate, causing anxiety (obsession) and coupled with repetitive actions or behaviors performed to reduce the anxiety (compulsions)

Symptoms: Individual recognizes that this thoughts and/or behaviors are unreasonable; for example, the person who wishes to stop checking and rechecking an alarm clock at night but feels unable to stop the repetitive behavior

Post traumatic-stress disorder

Definition: After exposure to a significant, life threatening event, the experience of anxiety symptoms in which the event is re-experienced through recollections

Symptoms: Recurrent recollections, dreams, hallucinatory-like flashbacks, impairment of social functioning

Chapter 4 - Diagnosis

Anxiety disorders are often exhausting chronic conditions, which can be present from an early age or begin suddenly after a triggering event. They are prone to flare up at times of high stress.

A good assessment is essential for the first diagnosis of an anxiety disorder, preferably using a standardized interview or questionnaire procedure alongside expert evaluation and the views of the affected person.

There should be a medical examination to identify possible medical conditions that can cause the symptoms of anxiety. A family history of anxiety disorders is often suggestive of the possibility of an anxiety disorder. Although rare, it is important to exclude the possibility of a neuroendocrine tumor of the medulla of the adrenal glands. The presence of a such a tumor is normally accompanied by paroxysms of headache, sweating, palpitations, and hypertension.

It is important to note that a patient with an anxiety disorder will often display symptoms of Clinical Depression and vice versa. Rarely does a patient show symptoms of only one or the other.

Tip:

Get a complete physical, including a check of your thyroid, blood iron levels and vestibular system. This can be a big help in ruling out some of your biggest fears. Once you have had your physical, remind yourself that you are healthy.

Self Tests

When it comes to making a diagnosis consulting your doctor is usually the best place to start. Your doctor will take a careful history, perform a physical examination, and order laboratory tests as needed.

• If you have another medical condition that you know about, there may be an overlap of signs and symptoms between what is old and what is new.

• Just determining that anxiety is psychological does not immediately identify the ultimate cause.

Often, finding out the cause requires involving a psychiatrist, clinical psychologist, or other mental-health professional.

Nevertheless if you think you might be a victim of an anxiety disorder you might want to do a self-test. If you find it difficult to discuss your anxiety with your doctor it might be helpful to score a self-test (on the internet) and print the score. You can use this score to discuss your worries with the doctor.

There are several tests you can find on the internet. Just search for "anxiety tests" using your favorite search engine.

For instance:

http://tinyurl.com/36kmdd

This test is designed to evaluate your general level of anxiety. Examine the statements in the test and point out how often you feel that way.

http://tinyurl.com/2lj8l6

This test will discover whether you should consider seeking help, and to what degree. For each statement in the questionnaire, you should indicate how often you feel that way. After finishing the test, you will receive a Snapshot Report with an introduction, a graph and a personalized interpretation for one of your test scores. You will then have the choice to buy the full results.

http://tinyurl.com/2kucfu

After taking this test, you will be able to tell if you show signs of suffering from one or more anxiety disorders.

Note: Don't be alarmed by these strange looking web site addresses. I have used them so you don't have to manually copy the long urls.

Warning:

In no way should the (online) tests you take be considered a complete or fully accurate psychological portrait.

Always go to a (mental) health professional for a sound advice and thorough diagnosis.

Chapter 5 - What Causes Anxiety Disorders?

So is there one set thing that causes anxiety disorders? When I was diagnosed a big thing for me was trying to find out what can cause it. I felt I could understand my issue if I knew why it was happening to me. Was there a gene I was born with or a gene I was missing? Was it something I learned growing up? Or was it my body's way of telling me I was under too much stress?

I found out there is no easy simple reason for why people develop anxiety. In fact all the reasons I listed above could have contributed to my anxiety. It is a bit on the complicated side. There are several reasons why an anxiety disorder might be brought on. It could be heredity, biology, family background, recent stress levels, your personal beliefs and your ability to express feelings or chemical imbalances.

Long Term, Predisposing Causes

Studies have shown that there are three major long term predisposing factors playing a role in the cause of anxiety disorders. Cumulative stress over time, childhood circumstances and heredity factors.

Heredity

While studies have shown that 15 to 25% of children who have parents who suffer from agoraphobia wind up suffering from it themselves, doctors are quick to say that these numbers are because it can be a learned condition. Meaning that if a child witnesses his or hers parent being afraid to step into an elevator, they might grow up with the same fear.

However you can inherit a general personality type that can predispose you to be excessively anxious which can lead to an anxiety disorder.   I have a grandmother who suffers from anxiety, while I didn't inherit the anxiety disorder from her because it is two different kinds. I more than likely inherited the gene that she might carry that makes me more prone to anxiety. We are the only two people in my family to suffer from anxiety; however both my mother and brother have stomach issues when they are faced with stressful situations. This isn't to say that everyone who has an anxiety disorder in their family will have one also.

Childhood Circumstances

There are some things that can happen in your childhood that can put you at a risk for developing anxiety. I'm not saying that everyone who might experience one of these circumstances develops a disorder, but they can be at an increased risk. Nor am I saying the parents are at fault here either. While I had some of the same circumstances growing up, it is unfair for me to blame my parents for my disorder.

Children who grow up in an environment that is overly cautious can be at a risk because they tend to worry excessively and be too concerned with safety. Children who are criticized a lot and have a lot expected from them tend to become very self critical as adults and feel that they are never good enough. In fact children who have low self-esteem have a high risk of developing an anxiety disorder when they are older. They might grow up being afraid of being rejected or that people won't like them. So they create a persona of whom they "should" be and not what they are. Living a life like this is stressful. No one is perfect, yet these children grow up believing that they should be. They never say no to anyone or anything even when they want to. Eventually the anxiety is the body's way of trying to tell them to take a break.

This is one of the reasons why some therapists find it so important to talk about your childhood and resolve some of the unresolved issues that some people may so they can move forward with their recovery. For me, it never worked and I always felt that what is in the past, should stay in the past. Other people may feel differently and benefit greatly from treatment like this.

Cumulative Stress Over Time

Everyone has stress. There is just no way to avoid it. Morning traffic can cause stress, and your job can cause stress, sometimes just deciding what to make for dinner can cause stress. Stress is an everyday part of life. However when stress persist without a break it tends to build up. It is more just than your normal everyday stress. It could be problems with your relationship, your health or money that last for a number of years. People living in Western society are experiencing more stress than they have at any previous time in history, and it is this stress that probably explains the increased occurrence of anxiety disorders.

Anxiety can also be caused by going through many life events in a short amount of time. There is a life events survey that many doctors use to gain an indication of the possible stress level   you might have accumulated over a 2-year span. They list stressful situations and score each one. The highest being death of a spouse, the lowest being a minor violation of the law. You are to find out which of these events you have experienced within the 2-year period and then tally up your score. If you score under 150, you are less likely to be suffering from the effects of cumulative stress. A score from 151-300 means you could be suffering from chronic stress depending on how you handled the life event that took place and you might benefit from relaxation techniques. Anything over 300 means you are more than likely experiencing some harmful effects of the stress.
When I filled this survey out my score was well over 300! I had

34

lost my father, my job, moved to a new place to live, had my mother get remarried, start a new relationship, start a new job, quit that job and started a new one, and moved in with someone all in the span of two years. Is it any wonder why I was having panic attacks.

Life Events Survey

Death of spouse	100
Divorce	73
Marital separation	65
Jail term	63
Death of close family member	63
Personal injury or illness	53
Marriage	50
Being fired from work	47
Marital problems	45
Retirement	45
Change in health of family member	44
Pregnancy	40
Sexual difficulties	39
Gain of new family member	39
Business readjustment	39
Change in finances	38
Death of close friend	37
Change to different line of work	36
Change in number of arguments with spouse	35
Mortgage or loan for major purchase such as a home)	31
Foreclosure of mortgage or loan	30
Change in responsibilities at work	29
Son or daughter leaving home	29
Trouble with in-laws	29
Outstanding personal achievement	28

Beginning or finishing school	26
Change in living conditions	25
Revision of personal habits	24
Trouble with boss	23
Change in work hours or conditions	20
Change in residence	20
Change in school	20
Change in recreation	19
Change in church activities	19
Change in social activities	18
Mortgage or loan for lesser purchase (such as a car or tv)	17
Change in sleeping habits	16
Change in number of family get-together's	15
Change in eating habits	15
Vacation	13
Christmas	12
Minor violations of the law	11

Note: It has been shown that stress is accumulated over time. Having one major life event might raise your stress level (for example 50) but it takes possibly 12 months under normal conditions to reduce this previous levels again. Many people don't realize that something else happening during this 'recovery' period will add to the level taking it even higher. The higher the level the more likely it is that you will experience negative or even physically damaging affects. Even minor levels of stress suffered over a prolonged period can lead to stress related problems but higher levels can lead to physical ailments and more severe psychological disorders.

Many people do handle stress differently than others. There are some people out there who can let stress just roll off their backs and never get panicky at all. There are others who thrive on stress and it encourages them to do more. Other Some people have so much stress in their lives that they can't handle it even if they tried. These are the people who are more prone to anxiety than other people. They cannot let the worries of their day go. It keeps them awake at night and they cannot focus on any other activities other than what is causing them the stress.

Chemical Imbalances - Biological

A chemical imbalance can be the cause of a number of mental illnesses. Not only anxiety but also depression, ADHD and bipolar disorders. While no doctor is 100% sure what cause a chemical imbalance they have found that these common types of imbalances affect people's mental health.

• Availability of neurotransmitters like serotonin, dopamine, Norepinephrine, GABA and acetylcholine

• Increased levels of toxic neurochemicals

• Lower levels of Magnesium, Zinc, or Potassium

• Low Levels of vitamins like B6, B9, B12 (all stress reducing vitamins) and Vitamin-C

• Undersupply of key cofactors like amino acids that are used to help transport neurotransmitter forerunners into the blood-brain barrier.

• Increased cortisol hormone levels.

Lately in the medical profession, doctors seem quick to decide that a chemical imbalance is what causes anxiety disorders. So let's get back to the question of what causes a chemical imbalance. Over the years several possible reasons have been given for the imbalance such as genetic factors or irregular brain development. Some researchers follow the theory that your own thoughts and actions can cause this imbalance. However it seems almost impossible to come up with conclusive evidence.

37

But why are many doctors nevertheless inclined to say that you may have a chemical imbalance causing your anxiety disorder if they are not a hundred percent sure what it is? This could be credited to a number of reasons. Most likely it is because a chemical imbalance can be easily treated with medication.

So besides the three long-term, predisposing causes there is also a fourth, a chemical imbalance, that can cause or help contribute to your anxiety disorder.

Short-Term, Triggering Causes

Long term causes such as heredity, childhood environment, and cumulative stress create a predisposition to anxiety disorders. Yet it often takes more specific conditions, operating over a short period of time, to actually trigger panic attacks or cause a phobia to develop.

Significant personal loss, significant life change, stimulants such as caffeine or nicotine, or the drugs marijuana or psilocybin, can act as triggers.

Maintaining Causes

Maintaining Causes of anxiety disorders can be several things. For instance avoidance of panic provoking situations or environments, anxious/negative self-talk ("what if thinking"), mistaken beliefs ("these symptoms are harmful and/or dangerous"), withheld feelings, lack of assertiveness.

These behaviors impede your healing and stop you from enjoying an anxiety-free life. Recognizing these barriers can be a great first step toward getting rid of your problems.

For instance anxious/negative self-talk. When you are obsessively negative, it means that you have a tendency toward being "negative" about people, places, situations, and things in your life.

Perhaps you find yourself saying things like "I can't do this!" or "No one understands!" or "Nothing ever works!", for example. You may be doing this unconsciously, but essentially you have what's known as a "sour grapes" attitude, and it holds you back from knowing what it's like to view life from a positive lens and enjoy the beauty in yourself and people around you! There's a whole world out there for you...with happiness and positive thinking.

When you engage in obsessive perfectionism, you are centered on trying to do everything "just so" to the point of driving yourself into an anxious state of being. You may find yourself making statements such as, "I have to do this right, or I'll be a failure!" or "If I am not precise, people will be mad at me!" Again, this behavior may be under the threshold of your awareness, but it interferes greatly with your ability to enjoy things without feeling "uptight" and "stressed."

When you are obsessed about analyzing things, you find yourself wanting to rehash a task or an issue over and over again. For instance, you might find yourself making statements such as, "I need to look this over, study it, and know it inside and out...or else I can't relax!" or "If I relax and let things go without looking them over repeatedly, things go wrong!"

While analytical thinking is an excellent trait, if it's done in excess you never get to stop and smell the roses because you're too busy trying to analyze everything and everyone around you. Gaining insight into this behavior is one of the most important keys to letting go of stress, and getting complete power over your anxiety.

39

If you find yourself engaging in any of the above behaviors, there are two things you can do to help yourself. First, ask the people you know, love, and trust, "Am I negative about things?", "Do I complain a lot?", and "Am I difficult to be around?"

This may be hard for you to listen to, as the truth sometimes hurts a great deal. But the insight you will get from others' assessment of you is invaluable, and you'll know precisely how others see you. Accept their comments as helpful info, and know that you will gain amazing insights from what you hear.

Second, keep a journal to write down and establish patterns of when you are using "hurtful behaviors." Even if you are not thrilled with the idea of writing, you can make little entries into a notebook or journal each day. The great part is that you'll begin to see patterns in your behavior that reveal exactly what you're doing to prevent yourself from curing your anxiety.

Now what more can you do to treat your anxiety disorder.

Chapter 6 - Treatment

The choices of treatment include cognitive behavioral therapy, lifestyle changes, and/or pharmaceutical therapy (medications). Mainstream treatment for anxiety consists of the prescription of anxiolytic agents and/or antidepressants and/or referral to a cognitive-behavioral therapist. Treatment controversy arises because some studies suggest that a combination of the medications and behavioral therapy can be more effective than either one alone. In children, the World Health Organization says that cognitive behavioral therapy in the form of the Friends for Life Program is best practice to treat anxiety.

The right treatment may depend much on the individual's genetics and environmental factors. Therefore it is important to work closely with a psychiatrist, therapist or counselor who is familiar with anxiety disorders and current treatments.

Several drugs can be prescribed to treat these disorders. These include benzodiazepines (such as Xanax), antidepressants of most of the main classes (SSRI, TCAs, MAOIs), and possibly Quetiapine.

What helped me most was a combination of pills (briefly a tranquilizer followed by an antidepressant in combination with therapy). However there is no best cure fitting all. It's a personal journey to learn how to cope with anxiety or to beat it.

Medication for Anxiety

Medication can be very useful in treating anxiety disorders and is often used in combination with other forms of therapy, such as cognitive-behavioral therapy. The most important aspect of the process of beginning a medication is to have an open and honest discussion with your physician, followed by ongoing evaluation and monitoring.

Benzodiazephines

When I was in the hospital I was given Xanax. Xanax is a high-potency benzodiazepine (BZs). Xanax and other drugs of this nature like Ativan and Klonopin slow down the central nervous system and decreases anxiety. It relaxes you. Xanax and other BZs work very quickly. Most people usually feel the symptoms subsiding after only 15-20 minutes. I used to tell myself if I could hold on for a half hour after taking a Xanax it would be all right. Another plus to this is that it can be taken on an as needed basis. You can take a small dose of it before you face a challenging situation. I'm claustrophobic so the first time I went for my MRI and MRA, I had to stop before they could even start because I was so scared. In case you never had one before, they insert your upper body into a tube like tunnel that is very small and tight. When I went back to try again, I took a Xanax to help reduce my fears and was able to make it through the whole procedure.

There are also hardly any side effects for many people when compared to antidepressants. Although some people have reported feeling sleepy the day after taking the Xanax or experience headaches.

However, Xanax and other BZs are addictive, which is why they should be taken on an as needed only basis. The higher the dosage and the more you take it, the harder it will be to get off it. Withdrawal from these medications can be difficult although there has been some studies that show Klonopin has less severe withdrawal symptoms than Xanax. If you wean yourself off any BZs to quickly you might experience what is known as rebound anxiety but the symptoms will be greater than the ones you initially experienced. Most people should wean themselves off it slowly over a period of six months or so if they find they are addictive to it. If you are addictive to it, talk to your doctor to come up with a plan of action to wean yourself off it.

Tip:

Keep in mind that any decision about taking medication is highly personal. It should only be made in conjunction with your mental health professional. Ask about the types of prescriptions available, their effectiveness, dosages and side effects so you have a good understanding of what to expect.

Another disadvantage to BZs is that they are effective only while you are taking them. After you stop taking them there is a 100% chance your anxiety will return unless you have learned how to handle difficult situations and made some changes to help you achieve long-term anxiety relief.

In my experience with Xanax, I never had a problem with it becoming addictive because I worked on trying to find other ways without medications to deal with my attacks. There were a few time when I could not calm myself down enough to ride the attack out that I did need to take a Xanax but it was never a routine for me. In fact after the first few months or so, I barely touched the stuff. There are some people who can take Xanax and not become addictive to it and others who do become addictive to it and need their doctors help weaning from it.

How Do Drugs For Anxiety Work

Chemical substances in the brain called neurotransmitters help messages pass from nerve to nerve. When a person is anxious, certain neurotransmitters become imbalanced and the brain becomes abnormally active. Drugs can be used to block or slow down this increased activity and thereby relieve the physical nature of the anxiety.

• Benzodiazepines.
  These increase the actions of a particular neurotransmitter in the brain called GABA, high levels of which slow down the

overactive brain. One example is diazepam, better known as Valium.

• Buspirone
This scales down activity in the brain by decreasing the effects of the neurotransmitter serotonin. It has fewer side effects than the benzodiazepines, although it takes longer to work.

• Beta-blockers
These drugs interfere with neurotransmitters in the brain, heart, and muscles to reduce the physical symptoms of anxiety such as palpitations and tremor. The most commonly used beta-blocker is propranolol.

What are the adverse effects?

The main drawback of the benzodiazepines is that they can cause drowsiness, and in some people, dizziness and confusion, so they should only be used in the short term. Also, if these drugs are used for a long time, the dose can become ineffective and dependence may develop.

Buspirone does not carry the risk of dependence, bur occasionally people experience dizziness, headaches, or stomach ulcers.

Beta-blockers are generally well tolerated but can cause coldness of the fingers and toes, and sleep disturbances.

SSRI Antidepressant Medications

Selective serotonin reuptake inhibitors or SSRI as they are commonly known contain some of the well-known antidepressants such as Prozac, Zoloft, Lexapro, Paxil, Luvox and Celexa. They are the first choice medications that are used by most doctors to treat anxiety disorders. As we said earlier, a cause of anxiety disorders could be a chemical imbalance cause by lack of neurotransmitters like serotonin. SSRIs increase levels of serotonin in the brain by preventing the reabsorption of it in the spaces between the nerve cells. By doing that the number of serotonin receptors on the brain cells decrease and become less sensitive to changes in the neurochemicals environment of the brain that is caused by stress. This usually takes about two months to take place which is why you won't feel an instant change when beginning one of these medications.

SSRIs are used most often to treat panic, panic with agoraphobia and obsessive compulsive disorder. Occasionally they will be used to treat post traumatic stress disorder, especially if it is accompanied by depression. Usually a person on an SSRI will have to take it for 1 to 2 years to feel the full effect of it. A common myth about antidepressants is that people become addictive on them, this is not true. They are not addictive. Another misconception is that they lead to weight gain, again this is not true.

There are some drawbacks to using these medications. As with almost any medication there is always a risk of side effects and SSRIs are not different. Some of the common side effects are jitteriness, restlessness, dizziness, drowsiness, headaches, nausea and a decreased sexual drive. These usually go away within two weeks of starting the medication. Relapse is low with SSRIs when compared with BZs. Another drawback is that it could take up to a month or more before people start seeing any real benefit from taking it. This is why sometimes your doctor might prescribe you a BZ like Xanax to help you get through the first month or so. This is the biggest complaint from people is that they did not get results from the medications fast enough so they went off them and their symptoms returned. I was given the alternative of taking Lexapro but any medication without the Xanax was not an option for me. Medication has been a lifesaver for many people and has kept them sane, but again it is not for everyone.

Tricyclic Antidepressants

These antidepressants included Tofranil, Pamelor, Norpramin, Anafranil and Sinequian among others. They are commonly used to treat panic attacks. They reduce both the frequency and intensity of the panic attacks in people. They can also help reduce depression that sometimes comes with panic attacks. Anafranil seem to be helpful in treating OCD.

The problem is Tricyclics have worse side effects than say the SSRIs. In fact they are not used that much at all when compared to SSRIs. There were studies done of imipramine and one third of the subjects had to drop out because they could not tolerate the side effects. The side effects included dry mouth, blurred vision, dizziness that can be caused by hypertension, weight gain, and sexual dysfunction can occur. Some people complain that anxiety can actually increase the first few days of taking this drug. The problem is that even though most of these side effects do go away after the first week or so, there were still 25% to 30% of people who continue to have the side effect even after the first few weeks. Also, almost half of the people who use these antidepressants relapse after stopping use of this drug.

MAO-Inhibitor Antidepressants

If you have tried everything else and found no relief, your doctor may try this class of antidepressant. MAO-Inhibitors are the oldest class of medications and Nardil is the most common one used for panic. These are effective antidepressants but usually last to use because of the risks they contain. They can cause a serious and sometimes fatal rise in blood pressure with they are combined with certain foods, cheeses and wine and some over-the-counter medications.

They do have a potent panic-blocking effect and are usually effective when all other options fail but some doctors feel that the side effects are not worth it. Besides common side effects like weight gain, low blood pressure, sexual dysfunction, headaches, fatigue and tiredness. However dietary restrictions are very important when you are on MAO-Inhibitors. You have to take extra caution to avoid any foods with tyramine which means that most cheeses are out, homemade yogurts, alcoholic, aged meats, fish, bananas, and some vegetables. You also have to stop taking over-the-counter cold medicines and antihistamines.

As you can see there are many options when it comes to taking medications, but how do you know if medications are for you. First, talk with your doctor to express any concerns you may have. You should consider these personal factors also; the severity of your problem, your personal feeling on taking medications, and your patience. As I have stated, you might not benefit from the medications for some time. Will you be able to wait that long for some relief?

Next you should look at how long you are going to be willing to take the medication. It is hard to say how long you will need to take it. Usually it depends on some factors.

You should find out what type of medication you will be taking. BZs and some beta-blockers should be used on an "as needed" basis. While antidepressants are usually recommended to take for at least six months, most people stay on them for anywhere from 1 to 2 years if not longer. Some people might even decided to stay on them but a lower dosage for longer than that.

Also consider what type of anxiety you have. If your anxiety is mild you might only need to take the medication for a short time while you learn ways to deal with your anxiety natural. Other people who are having frequent panic attacks will

47

probably need to take their medication for a longer time. If you suffer from OCD, a long-term use of an SSRI medication is usually recommended. Usually about 2 years or more before the dosage could be lowered to see what dosage might work best for you need to correct the neurobiological problem that accompanies OCD. The more severe the disorder, the longer you should stay on the medication.

You also need to see if you can eliminate or at least reduce your need for medication at least in the long run. If you follow a program of natural approaches and stick with it, your brain can recover. You just have to be motivated and committed to the natural approaches that we will touch on later. When you decide to stop relying on medication there are some guidelines you should keep in mind before you stop. The first one is to make sure you have gained experience with the basic strategies for overcoming anxiety and panic. For example, if you have established a daily practice of deep relaxation and exercise. Second, make sure you talk to your doctor to see if he wants to set up a program for you to follow to taper off the drugs especially if you are stopping any BZ. Next, be prepared to depend on more natural techniques to get through the panic attacks and last do not be disappointed if you need to rely on the medication again for periods of anxiety and stress. You might find that short-term use of the medication you stopped might be helpful during certain time of the year especially if you are like me.

My panic disorder tends to intensify during the winter months and although I haven't taken Xanax in almost 3 years, I make sure to keep some just in case.

Medication is not for everyone and if it does not work for you, do not feel like a failure. There are plenty of other options when dealing with anxiety disorders.

Therapy

There are several treatments that have proven to be most successful in treating the various Anxiety Disorders. I have listed the several treatment options along side with the disorders that are most regularly treated with them. This contents of this table however can not be leading in the treatment. You should always find out what suits you best in dialogue with a (mental) health care professional.

Combination Therapy

In many cases it would appear that the ideal treatment for anxiety disorders is a combination of medication and therapy.

I have listed the most common treatments and the anxiety disorders in the table on the next page. You might find it helpful to find your way to the right therapist.

GAD = Generalized Anxiety Disorder
OCD = Obsessive Compulsory Disorders
PTSD = Post Traumatic Stress Disorder

	Panic Attacks	Agora-phobia	Social Phobia	Specific Phobia	GAD	OCD	PTSD
Relaxation Training	X	X	X	X	X	X	X
Cognitive Therapy		X	X	X	X	X	X
Medication	X	X	X			X	X
Exposure		X	X	X		X	X
Lifestyle and Personality Changes	X					X	
Assertiveness Training		X	X				
Panic-Control Therapy	X						
Interoceptive Desensitization	X						
Group Therapy							
Staying on task			X				
Social Skills Training			X				
Worry Exposure					X		
Reducing Worry Behaviors					X		
Problem Solving					X		
Distraction					X		
Mindfulness Practice					X		
Exposure and Response Prevention						X	
Support Groups							X
EMDR or Hypnotherapy							X

Relaxation Training

Practicing abdominal breathing and some form of deep muscle relaxation techniques (such as progressive muscle relaxation) on a daily basis. This helps to reduce the <u>physical</u> symptoms of panic as well as anticipatory anxiety you might experience about having a panic attack. It also helps to better control anxiety symptoms.

Cognitive Behavioral Therapy

Tip:

Always ask about cognitive-behavioral therapy. Experience has shown this therapy to be one of the most effective and long-lasting treatments available for people with anxiety disorders.

A Cognitive Behavioral Therapy (CBT) is a psychotherapy based on changing cognitions, assumptions, beliefs and behaviors, with the aim of influencing disturbed emotions. The general approach developed out of Cognitive Therapy has become widely used to treat various anxiety disorders. The particular therapeutic techniques vary according to the particular client or issue, but commonly include keeping a diary of significant events and associated feelings, thoughts and behaviors; questioning and testing cognitions, assumptions, evaluations and beliefs that might be unhelpful and unrealistic; gradually facing activities which may have been avoided; and trying out new ways of behaving and reacting.

There is strong evidence that behaviorally based treatments are effective in treating at least some anxiety disorders.

The aim of cognitive therapy is to help you replace exaggerated, fear thinking about panic and phobias with more realistic and supportive mental habits. When you worry, you overestimate the odds of something negative happening and underestimate your ability to cope if something bad did, in fact, happen.

While insight is very much involved in this process, it is not insight into deep psychological causes, as in psychoanalysis, but, rather, practical commonsense problem solving.

Some examples will illustrate the process:

• You learn identify, challenge, and replace counterproductive thoughts with helpful ones.

• Fearful thoughts that perpetuate social phobias are identified, challenged, and replaced with more realistic thoughts. For example, the thought "I'll make a fool of myself if I speak up" would be replaced with the idea "It's okay if I'm a bit awkward at first when I speak up-most people won't be bothered."

• Fearful thoughts that tend to perpetuate the specific phobia are challenged and replaced. For example, "What if I panic because I feel trapped aboard an airplane?" would be replaced with more realistic and supportive thoughts, such as, "While I may not be able to leave the airplane for two hours, I can move around, such as leaving my seat to go to the bathroom several times if needed.

• If I start to feel panicky, I have many strategies for coping that I can use, including abdominal breathing, talking to my companion, listening to a relaxing tape, or taking medication, if necessary."

• Coping statements, such as, "I've handled this before and I can handle it again" or "This is just a thought; it has no validity," are also useful.

These supportive coping statements are rehearsed until they are internalized.

Fearful, superstitious, or guilty thoughts associated with obsessions are identified, challenged, and replaced. For example, the idea "If I have a thought of doing harm to my child, I might act on it" is replaced with "The thought of doing harm is just 'random noise' caused by the OCD. It has no significance. Just having the thought doesn't mean I'll do it."

Fearful or depressed thinking is identified, challenged, and replaced with more productive thinking. For example, guilt about having been responsible for the trauma. Or having survived when someone you loved did not, would be challenged. You would reinforce yourself with supportive, constructive thoughts, such as, "What happened was horrible, and I accept that there is nothing I could have done to prevent it. I'm learning now that I can go on."

Cognitive behavioral therapy is not an overnight process. Even after patients have learned to recognize when and where their mental processes go awry, it can take months of effort to replace any dysfunctional cognitive-affective-behavioral processes or habit with a more reasonable, salutary one.

Friends For Life Program

Friends for Life helps children and teenagers cope with feelings of fear, worry, and depression by building resilience and self-esteem and teaching cognitive and emotional skills in a simple, well-structured format.

Used in schools and clinics throughout the world, FRIENDS is the only childhood anxiety prevention program acknowledged by the World Health Organization for its 8 years of comprehensive evaluation and practice. It has proved effective for up to 6 years after initial exposure.

The program is currently used in schools and clinics throughout Australia, New Zealand, Canada, the United Kingdom, Germany, the Netherlands, the United States, Mexico, Norway, and Portugal.

FRIENDS is run by a school's own teachers and does not involve any clinical assessment or diagnosis, thus avoiding labeling children as anxious or different.

Before starting a FRIENDS program, teachers attend a one-day group training workshop. These workshops are conducted regularly across Australia by Pathways Health and Research Centre and overseas by accredited training partners.

Anxiety is the most common form of mental disorder, affecting up to 15% of children and teenagers. Anxiety significantly interferes with a child's ability to confidently handle everyday situations, including relationships with peers, adults and family, and school achievement. If left unattended, anxiety difficulties may continue into young adulthood, sometimes leading to depression. FRIENDS combats anxiety by fostering an emotional resilience in children and teenagers that will stay with them for life.

Completing a 10-session FRIENDS program can reduce a child's risk of developing a disorder for up to six years. Children with normal levels of worry benefit by acquiring resilience to emotional stress.

FRIENDS promotes important personal development concepts such as self-esteem, problem-solving, self-expression, and building positive relationships with peers and adults, and therefore fits in well with the normal curriculum.

Helping Your Child Overcome Fear

Does your child suffer the detrimental effects of fear?

Fear is part of our emotional makeup that helps us to identify danger. When children sense that something is wrong, they may feel an intense anxiety, causing their heart rate and blood pressure to increase, as well as sweating, shaking or running away from their object of fear.

In cases where children are highly fearful, they may run to their parents with loud shrieks or screams. The sense of fear may not relate proportionally to the threat or danger that is evident. This is called "irrational fear". When fear stops a child from functioning in their normal environment, it has become a "phobia".

How are fears developed?

There are several ways that children develop fear. The child's first main contact with fear is usually developed by relating cause and effect. For instance, a loud noise like the discharge of a gun may cause a child to be afraid if they see negative effects resulting from the discharge. A child may run away to hide whenever they see a gun – avoiding the object of fear.

A second way that fear is developed in children is by observing the actions of others - usually their parents - and imitating them. For example, whenever a child sees a parent shriek or run away from a spider, the child learns that spiders are objects of fear.

Sometimes fears are developed when parents "reward" the child for showing a fearful response. For example, a child may avoid using a bath towel that has "germs" on it for fear of being contaminated. If a clean towel is given each time a child requests it because of "germs" then you really are only rewarding the fear response, rather than helping to solve the root cause.

How can parents help their child overcome fear?

1. Here are seven steps to help your child to overcome fear.

2. Don't model fearful reactions

3. Show them that you can handle difficult situations and don't need to avoid fearful situations

4. Teach your child how to cope with fearful situations

5. Praise your child when they cope rather than run away

6. Keep a calm atmosphere during unsettled periods

7. Stay firm and keep a positive outlook

8. Talk about genuine threats to provide a balanced view

Your children's fear can be reduced by working through the fearful situation directly with your child. By showing that you are able to handle fearful situations you can help your child to "outgrow" most fears that are common in children.

Exposure

Exposure therapy is suggested to be one of the best ways to overcome your anxiety. To master something in life it is necessary first to think about it, and then practice doing it. Remember when you first started to learn how to drive. The more you practiced the better you became. This is the basis of exposure therapy. You need to go into the situation and think about it in a different way, implement the other skills and knowledge you have to mange your anxiety, and then reflect on how it went.

There is a word of caution here. Some research suggests to 'face the fear and do it anyway'. For some people this may work, however for others it doesn't. Learning the skills and techniques of cognitive therapy and educating yourself on where your anxiety is coming from in the first place, before exposing yourself to the situation, can often have better outcomes as you can feel more in control before you enter the situation, rather than going in feeling terrified.

When you feel anxious, it is suggested that you go through it first in your mind (realistic thinking/skills of cognitive therapy), and second, put yourself in the situation that you fear. This part is called exposure therapy. For example, if you feared driving far from home, you would gradually increase the distance you drive in small increments. A support person might go with you in the same car, then drive in a second car behind you, and then, finally, you would practice driving alone. Or, if you were fearful of being home alone, the person who usually stays with you would leave for a few minutes at first and then gradually increase the time away. Over time you learn to confront, and enter into all of the situations you have been avoiding.

Another example in case of a social phobia could involve gradually and incrementally facing the social situation or situations you're phobic about. You might do this first in imagery and then in real life. For example, if you're phobic of public speaking, you might start out giving a one-minute talk to a friend and then gradually increase, through many steps, both the duration of what you say and the number of people you speak to. Or, if you have difficulty speaking up in groups, you'd gradually increase both the length and degree of self-disclosure of remarks made in a group setting. After each exposure, you'd review and challenge any unrealistic thinking that caused anxiety. While the treatment for social phobia can be done on an individual basis, group therapy is the ideal treatment format. This allows direct exposure to the situation and stimuli that evoke anxiety in the first place.

Fear of flying would be faced first in imagination only, then by watching planes land and take off, then by boarding a grounded plane, then by taking a short flight, and, finally, a

57

longer flight. A support person would accompany you first through all the steps, then you'd try them on your own.

For some phobias, it's difficult to do real-life exposure. For example, if you're afraid of earthquakes, treatment would emphasize cognitive therapy and then exposure to imagined scenes of earthquakes (or watching movies about earthquakes).

Lifestyle Changes

Some of the lifestyle changes that can reduce your tendency to have panic attacks include stress management, regular exercise, removing stimulants and sugar from your diet, slowing down and creating "downtime," and changing attitudes toward perfectionism,

an excessive need to please others, or the excessive need to control.

Some examples include:

- Learn To Relax: Find a relaxation technique that works for you and use it to combat stress. Use breathing techniques to manage attacks.

- Exercise: It doesn't have to be anything too strenuous, just get out there and take a walk, go for a swim, or do something to develop a regular exercise routine. Studies have shown that exercise has a positive effect on mental health.

- Get Plenty Of Sleep: This is important for maintaining health and for keeping stress levels down.

- Talk With A Friend: Talking about what is bothering you can help relieve stress.

- Practice Good Time Management: Good planning can remove needless worry and running around which in turn will help reduce stress.

- Remove Stressful Activities From Your Life: Identify what causes you stress and remove it from your lifestyle when possible.

- Watch Your Diet: Eat food high in calcium, magnesium, phosphorus, and potassium since these nutrients are depleted by stress. Limit meats and other animal proteins and eat lots of fruits, grains, and vegetables instead.

- Avoid Caffeine: Caffeine can trigger panic attacks so avoid coffee, chocolate, some sodas and some teas, and other products containing caffeine.

- Avoid Refined Sugars And Simple Carbohydrates: Cut simple sugars, carbonated soft drinks and alcohol out of the diet

Studies showed that those who made these lifestyle changes experienced less panic and anxiety in one month and needed less doctor treatments than did those who did not make lifestyle changes!

So take this advice seriously!

Assertiveness training

Since agoraphobics often have difficulty standing up for themselves and their rights, and lack the ability to ask directly for what they want or to say no to what they don't want. Assertiveness training, a behavior therapy in which people are taught fitting methods of asserting themselves in various situations through honest and direct expression of their feelings, is often part of the treatment.

Panic - Control Therapy

The general goal of PCT is to foster within patients the ability to identify and correct maladaptive thoughts (such as, "I'm trapped!", 'I'm going to go crazy!" or "I'm going to have a heart attack!") and behaviors that launch, sustain, or worsen anxiety and panic attacks. In service of that goal,, the treatment combines education, cognitive interventions, relaxation and controlled breathing procedures, and exposure techniques

Interoceptive Desensitization

Practicing voluntary habituation to the bodily symptoms of panic, such as rapid heartbeat, sweaty hands, shortness of breath, or dizziness. Such symptoms are created deliberately, usually in the therapist's office. For example, dizziness might be induced by spinning in a chair or rapid heartbeat by running up and down stairs. Repeated exposure to unpleasant bodily symptoms promotes desensitization, which means getting used to them so they no longer frighten you.

Group Therapy

Group Psychotherapy is a form of psychotherapy during which one or several therapists treat a small group of clients together as a group. This may be more cost effective than individual therapy, and possibly even more productive. Treatment for agoraphobia can be done effectively in a group setting. There is much support available in a group, both for realizing that you are not alone and for completing week-to-week homework assignments.

Staying On Task

People with social phobia focus a lot on how they are doing or try to gauge other people's reactions while speaking in a social situation. Treatment includes training yourself to focus only on the task at hand, whether conversing with a boss, speaking up in class, or presenting information to a group.

Social Skills Training

Social skills training (SST) is a form of behavior therapy used by teachers, therapists, and trainers to help anyone having difficulties relating to other people. Sometimes, learning basic social skills such as smiling and making eye contact, maintaining a conversation, self-disclosure, and active listening are part of the treatment for social phobia.

Worry Exposure

Worry exposure requires that you do repeated and prolonged exposure to fearful images (your worst-case scenarios) of what you're worried about. This helps you to become used to the worry, and help you experience that worrying and anxiety do not cause negative events. In worry exposure, In these images you include strategies you would use to reduce anxiety and cope with the situation.

Reducing Worry Behaviors

You identify overly cautious "safety behaviors" that reinforce worrying. Pick the easiest behavior to stop and predict results of stopping it. For example, if you call your spouse or child several times a day to check on them, you would reduce the frequency of this behavior.

Problem Solving

This means taking systematic action to solve the problem you're worried about.

Focus on solutions to the problem that worries you instead of the worry itself. If there is no practical solution, you work on changing your attitude toward the situation, that is, learning to accept what you can't change

Distraction

Use distraction to change your thoughts or despair to thoughts of relaxation. Remember, the more desperate one is to relax, the more difficult relaxation can be.

Luckily there are various distraction techniques that can be helpful for worries that do not lend themselves easily to cognitive therapy or problem solving. Common diversionary activities include talking to a friend, journaling, listening to music, gardening, exercise, puzzle solving, arts and crafts, cooking, and the Internet.

Tip:

Use humor whenever you can. Laughing is a great way to release stress. I bought the Fawlty Towers DVD box, a classic British sitcom from the 1970s set in a slightly crazy hotel, representing the height of the golden era of television comedy. Because it makes me laugh, again and again.

Mindfulness Practice

Mindfulness is an attitude of simply witnessing the endless stream of your thoughts and feelings in the present moment without judgment. It originated in Buddhist meditation practice but is now being used as a common treatment for stress, depression, and generalized, anxiety.

Exposure And Response Prevention (ERP

This technique consists of exposure to situations that aggravate obsessions, followed by enforced prevention from performing rituals or compulsions. For example, if you've been washing your hands every time you touch a doorknob, you'd be taught to touch doorknobs and either reduce the number of times you wash your hands or refrain from washing at all. Similarly, if you check the door five times whenever you leave your house, you would be required to gradually reduce the number of checks to one.

You and your therapist devise various situations, preferably in your home setting. Then you continually practice exposing yourself to these situations and give up on performing the compulsions (response prevention). Usually your therapist or a support person accompanies you to check your compliance in not performing compulsions.

When your problem involves obsessions only, without compulsions, any neutralizing thoughts or covert rituals you use to reduce anxiety caused by your obsessions need to be stopped.

You would also work on accepting your obsessions without trying to make them go away.

Support Groups

In a support group, members provide one another with various types of nonprofessional, nonmaterial help for a particular shared burdensome characteristic. The help may take the form of providing relevant information, relating personal experiences, listening to others' experiences, providing sympathetic understanding and setting up social networks. Support groups are helpful in enabling PTSD victims to realize that they are not alone. Support groups for rape or crime survivors are often available in larger metropolitan areas.

EMDR or Hypnotherapy

Eye-movement desensitization and reprocessing (EMDR) or hypnotherapy are often helpful in enabling PTSD victims to retrieve and work through memories of the original traumatic incident. These techniques may be used to speed up the course of therapy and/or overcome resistance to exposure.

Use Affirmations

Besides therapy and medication there are some things you can do yourself that might give you that extra push forward. I developed personal affirmations and positive statements about the progress I was making, no matter how great or how small. These were often related to my panic attacks but sometimes also about life in general.

You can always counter your negative thoughts with positive affirmations. These positive affirmations can build confidence and change negative behavior patterns into positive ones.

The key is to base your affirmations on a rational assessment of fact and use them to fight against the negative thinking that might have undermined your self-confidence. Here are some handy positive affirmations you might consider using.

• I can achieve my goals

• I can do this

• I am completely self-confident in every social situation

• I am completely myself, and people will like me

• I am in control of my life

• I am a valued person

Using positive affirmations can give you surprising strength but it isn't a cure for all ills. Decide rationally what goals you can re-

alistically reach with hard work. Use positive thinking to reinforce these goals.

Choosing The Right Mental Health Professional

You have several choices in selecting a mental health professional:

• psychiatrists

• psychologists

• clinical social workers

• other types of counselors

There are differences in the training and licensing re-
quirements among these professions, and choosing among them
can seem complicated. I don't want to complicate your job here,
so I'm going to offer you some simple advice on selecting one.

Not everyone will agree with my advice, and you should
assume it reflects my own biases.

Psychiatrists are doctors who specialize in mental health.
They generally use medication as their treatment method, because that is their area of specialty. Because the odds are high
that a psychiatrist will recommend medication to you, and will
probably be much less familiar with cognitive behavioral methods than will other practitioners, I suggest you select one of the
other professions for your first consultation. Of course, if you
want medication, you should go directly to a psychiatrist.

Which other profession? I think this is less important
than finding a professional who has some specialized training
and experience with the cognitive behavioral treatment of panic.

In major urban areas, such people are available, if you know how to look. In rural areas, unfortunately, there are often none.

Tips For A Support Person

If you are a 'support person' and you have a friend or a loved one suffering from panic attacks you would be surprised at how many people go to the hospital emergency room completely sure that they're having a heart attack only to find out that it's a panic attack. They're that intense!

It's very difficult for many people to imagine or even understand what somebody is going through when they have a panic attack. They may lose patience, tell this person to "get over it", or think the other is faking. To gain a better understanding of the victim of a panic attack try to imagine you are the main character in the following scenario.

You are standing in line at the grocery store. It's been a long wait but there's only one customer to go before you make it to the cashier. Wait, what was that?

An unpleasant feeling forms in your throat, your chest feels tighter, now a sudden shortness of breath, and what do you know--your heart skips a beat. "Please, God, not here."

You make a quick scan of the territory--is it threatening? Four unfriendly faces are behind you and one person is in front. Pins and needles seem to prick you through your left arm, you feel slightly dizzy, and then the explosion of fear as you dread the worst. You are about to have a panic attack.

There is no doubt in your mind now that this is going to be a big one. Okay, time for you to focus. You know how to deal with this – at least you hope you do! Start breathing deeply - in through the nose, out through the mouth.

Think relaxing thoughts, and again, while breathing in, think "Relax," and then breathe out. But it doesn't seem to be having any positive effect; in fact, just concentrating on breathing is making you feel self-conscious and more uptight.

Maybe if you just try to relax your muscles. Tense both shoulders, hold for 10 seconds, then release. Try it again. Nope, still no difference. The anxiety is getting worse and the fact that you are out of coping techniques worsens your panic. If only you were surrounded by your family, or a close friend were beside you so you could feel more confident in dealing with this situation.

Now, the adrenaline is pumping through your system, your body is tingling with uncomfortable sensations, and now the dreaded feeling of losing complete control engulfs your emotions. No one around you has any idea of the sheer terror you are experiencing. For them, it's just a regular day and another frustratingly slow line at the grocery store.

You realize you are out of options. It's time to run. You excuse yourself from the line looking embarrassed as it is now that it is your turn to pay. The cashier is looking bewildered as you leave your shopping behind and stroll towards the door.

There is no time for excuses--you need to be alone. You leave the supermarket and get into your car to ride it out alone. You wonder whether this one was the big one. The one you fear will push you over the edge mentally and physically. Ten minutes later the panic subsides. It's only 11:00 in the morning, how in the world can you make it through the rest of your day?

If you suffer from panic or anxiety attacks, the above scenario probably sounds familiar. It may have even induced feelings of anxiety and panic just reading it. In fact, it was difficult for me just to write it!

The particular situations that trigger your panic and anxiety may differ. Maybe the bodily sensations are a little different. What's important to realize is that panic attacks are very real to the people who are having them and they should never be pushed off to the side.

I remember one evening at home when I was by myself watching one of my favorite television programs. I thought I was in a safe place. There was no obvious trigger and I felt completely relaxed. Out of nowhere, I began having symptoms of a panic attack. The four walls of my living room were closing in around me. I couldn't breathe and felt like I was dying.

I stepped out on my front porch for some fresh air and began deep breathing exercises. The symptoms eventually went away, but it left me wondering why exactly I had that attack. There was no obvious reason, no stressful situation, and no indicator that a panic attack might be impending.

That's the strange thing about panic. Sometimes your mind can play tricks on you. Even when you think you're in no danger of having a panic attack, your brain might be feeling differently. That's the scary part.

My advice to people who care and would like to help somebody suffering from panic attacks would be to learn as much as you can about panic disorder. Then also know that you will probably have only about a 75% understanding of the panic anxiety. Ask the person with panic disorder to share how they feel, not during a panic attack, but rather when things are calm. Then find out what a panic attack is like for them.

• Just listen, don't try to solve the panic. As much as you, may want to, you can't fix it or take away the panic.

- Learn how you can support a person with panic disorder during an attack. It may mean just being there or giving them a hug. Those things can be more supportive than you may ever know.

- Let the person with panic disorder organize some activities that you can do together. You'll be surprised at how much they're willing to try if they can set their own parameters.

- Acknowledge those times when a panic sufferer sincerely says that they want to try to move forward or try activities despite their panic. Your support in this success can encourage them to try again.

- Compromise when possible. Be open to an adjustment that can easily be done that will make the outing successful and more comfortable. Change a departure time to avoid rush hour, take stairs instead of an elevator, and make adjustments for other, similar activities that are uncomfortable for the person with anxieties.

- Cancel plans under certain circumstances, if necessary. When you do make the decision to cancel, accept that decision and do it without guilt or accusations.

- Share your feelings as a support person. Good two-way communication can go a long way toward helping you both through the tough times.

- Work on keeping your relationship focused on the person you know and love. Understand that they are going through tough times, and care for them as you would in any other circumstance when they would need your help.

- Seek your own professional counseling. Living with someone with any type of disorder is going to bring up your own emotions and issues. Encourage the person with panic disorder to participate in a program for graduated exposure therapy. Offer to help them as a buddy to lean on during the initial and tough stages.

• Be a buddy or safe person. Be willing to be gentle and yet a bit firm. Encourage and comfort while helping the person focus on the task at hand. This is a specific role and may not be for everyone.

Chapter 7 - Natural Supplements

If you are a little weary of taking prescribed medications, you might find some benefit in taking a natural supplement. There are many supplements that are available at your local drugstore. Most people find supplements beneficially if their condition is not out of control but is more of a nuisance in their life.

Kava is one of the most recommended anti anxiety supplements. It is usually found in the pacific. Most people who have used kava report that they feel relaxation minus the drugged feeling, a sense of peacefulness, they find that they are more sociable and initially feel an alertness that can be followed a few hours later by drowsiness so it is ok to take in the evening. The one thing to remember about Kava is that it cannot be taken every day. It should only be taken no more than three times a week and you should always give yourself one week off the Kava. The most common side effects are tiredness and decreased sex drive.

Another common natural supplement is St. Johns Wort. St. Johns Wort or Hypericium as it is sometimes also referred to has been said to be nature's Prozac. It promises to treat depression and anxiety but without any of the side effects of prescription medications. St John's Wart has been used for years as a folk remedy for depression, only back then it went by its name Hypericium perforatum. Besides being used for depression, it also has a history of being used for muscle pain, high blood pressure, stomach problems and even cancer. Unfortunately there is no date right now on how St. John's Wort woks with the brain though some experts think it changes the balance of chemicals the same way and SSRI's or MAO inhibitors do. There are some side effect with St. John's Wort. Some people become more sensitive to the sun; have headaches, dizziness, dry mouth and constipation. Another thing to keep in mind is that you should not take St. Johns Wort if you are on oral birth control pills. Studies have shown that St. John's Wort decreases the effectiveness of the pill.

Many of these supplements such as Kava and St. John Wort along with several others like Passion Flower, and Valerian are used more than prescribed antidepressants because most people report feeling the better after a week or so on the natural supplements vs. a few weeks or more on the prescribe medication.

Tip:

If you are pregnant or have health problems, check with your doctor before taking herbs.

There is however one supplement that is very different from St. Johns Wort and Kava and that is SAM-e (S-adenosyl-methionine). SAM-e differs from them and other herbs that are used for depression because it is something occurs naturally in our bodies. SAM-e increases serotonin and dopamine activity in the brain. Some doctors believe that people who are lacking enough SAM-e in their bodies are usually clinically depressed or suffer from anxiety. Another pro with SAM-e is there are almost no side effects aside for some queasiness the first few days of taking it. SAM-e also works fast. Most people will feel better within a few days of taking it. Not only does it help with depression and anxiety but it also helps with joint pain and liver function.

Warnings:

Individual using prescribed medication such as antidepressant, including Serotonin Re-Uptake Inhibitors and MAO Inhibitors should consult a doctor before using. Individuals with Parkinson's disease, bi-polar disorder or manic depression should not use SAM-e.

To be sure if SAM-e is safe to use consult your doctor.

Medications will work best for people who are suffering from OCD and PTSD but those who suffer from panic disorders might find it more helpful to rely on other methods to manage their panic instead of medication. There is no set cure for panic attacks, but learning how to manage them will help decrease the occurrence. Read on to find out how to manage your panic and anxiety.

Chapter 8 - Nutrition and Anxiety

We've been spending much time talking about medications or herbs that can help with anxiety disorders, but let's take some time now to look at some lifestyle changes you can make to help you deal with anxiety disorders.

Can a good diet help your anxiety disorder. According to research done for the past twenty years, the answer is yet. It has been shown that certain food can create more stress and anxiety and others can create a sense of calmness. For years nutritionists have been trying to tell us that what we put in our bodies food wise, can have a direct effect on our emotions and it is about time that we start to listen to them.

Tip:

Don't skip meals, especially breakfast. Make sure you eat three healthy meals each day.

Caffeine

The first thing you should look at is if you are taking in too much caffeine. Caffeine is famous for triggering panic attack. In fact the more coffee I drank, the worse my attacks were. I was a sodaholic. I could drink a 2 liter bottle of soda in a matter of hours regardless of the time. It wasn't until I started trying to learn other ways to control my panic attacks that I cut back on caffeine and when I became pregnant with my first child, I cut down even more and became so sensitive to caffeine that if I had even one glass of tea or soda with caffeine after 3pm. I was up all night.

This is because caffeine increases the levels of neurotransmitters in your brain and that can cause you to feel alert and awake. It can also produce the same response as when you are faced with stress and that is a release of adrenaline. Caffeine can keep some people in a state of tension. How many times have you heard someone say about someone who is jumpy and jittery that they should "lay off the caffeine" while this is only an expression, it is a true statement about some people.

Now you might be reading this saying that you never drink coffee so this does not refer to you, but caffeine is not just in coffee. You can find caffeine in tea, sodas, chocolate candy, cocoa and many over-the-counter drugs like Excedrin. Also, do not let the words Decaffeinated fool you. Did you know that de-caffeinated coffee contains 4 milligrams a cup? That might not seem a lot but think about how many cups you drink and add it up. Out of all the soda's Coca-Cola has the most amount of caffeine, almost as much as a cup of instant coffee, Cola has 65 mg while instant coffee has 66 mg. If you drink a lot of caffeine, it is recommended that you limit your caffeine intake to 100 mg a day. Use the figures below to figure out how much caffeine you consume in a day.

Instant Coffee- 66 mg
Coffee Drip- 146 mg
Teabag- 5 minute brew- 46 mg
Teabag- 1 minute brew- 28 mg
Cocoa- 13 mg
Coca-Cola- 65 mg
Dr. Pepper- 61 mg
Mountain Dew- 55 mg
Diet Dr. Pepper- 54 mg
Diet Coke- 49 mg
Pepsi Cola- 43 mg.

Take caution though when reducing caffeine especially if you consume a lot of it. Some people do have sensitivity to caffeine and might experience withdrawal symptoms such as headaches, and fatigue. If you drink five cups of coffee a day, you might want to start reducing that amount slowly over a period of a few months to reduce the withdrawal symptoms.

Tip

When you start to crave that coffee buzz, try pouring some sparkling water into your mug and sip on that. Keep sipping: most of us don't get enough water anyway.

Nicotine

This is a strong stimulant that can play tricks on your mind. As an ex-smoker I can tell you it took a long time for me to realize that cigarettes were contributing to my conditioning not helping it. I like many smokers often used smoking to calm my nerves when in reality nicotine does the opposite. Sure at first there is a calming effect, but that is more in your head. Nicotine speeds up your heart rate and can lead to more panic attacks and problems sleeping.

The hardest part about quitting is the withdrawal symptoms, especially if you quit cold turkey. If you quit cold turkey, you might find that your panic symptoms increase for at least for the first week or so while the nicotine exits your system. This is due to your body's chemistry trying to correct itself and because of the mental withdrawal most smokers go through. I quit cold turkey and it was the hardest thing I have ever done, but I stuck with it. There are however many quit aids out that can help you make your quitting easier. There are nicotine replacement therapy drugs such as the nicotine patch, and nicotine gum that can slowly wean you off the nicotine. Then there are also some medications such as Zyban and Wellbutrin which are antidepressants that can help you with the withdrawal symptoms of quitting. While nicotine is not considered part of a diet, it does have to do with your bodies overall health and that is why it is included in this portion

Sugar

We know that our bodies need sugar to survive. Sugar is our body's gas. Our bodies need the naturally occurring sugar that is called glucose to provide us with energy.

However how fast the glucose forms in your body can play an important role in our health. Most carbohydrates such as some breads, potatoes, vegetables, fruits and pastas contain starches that are slowly broken down into glucose while other foods that contain simple sugars like honey, white sugar and brown sugar along with candies break down quickly into glucose and overload us with it. Unfortunately almost all of us probably eat too much of this refined sugar daily because it is everywhere. It is in soft drinks, cereal, salad dressings, and even some meats. Studies have shown that the average person eats about 120 pounds of sugar a year. In some people this overload of glucose can lead to diabetes which is too high levels of sugar in the body, but it can also lead to the opposite when your blood sugar drops below normal levels. These people suffer from hypoglycemia. The symptoms of hypoglycemia strongly resemble the symptoms of a panic attack. If you suffer from hypoglycemia you might find yourself feeling light-headed, trembling, experiencing palpitations and even a more heighten sense of anxiety a few hours after eating a meal.

While there are some people who developed panic attacks from being hypoglycemic, it is not always the cause of panic attacks. Usually the hypoglycemia is just another issue that can bring on a panic attack. Correcting hypoglycemia is easy to correct simply by making some big changes to your diet. You could start by cutting out all types of simple sugars from your diet. No more cookies, candy, soda, and ice-cream to name a few. You will have to start reading the labels on your food to make sure they do not have high fructose either. Start eating more fruit but stay away from fruit juices as they are made with a lot of sugar.

You also want to start eating more complex carbohydrates. Instead of eating pasta and white bread, add whole grain breads, brown rice, vegetables and even whole wheat pasta to your diet. Another adjustment is add either a complex carb or protein snack between your meals. This should not be anything too big, but a few nuts or a slice of cheese will be fine to help keep your sugar level even.

Another way to help correct it, is by taking supplements such as Vitamin B-Complex and Vitamin C once a day with your meals. These will help increase your resiliency to stress. Stress can create blood sugar swings which can increase anxiety.

Stressful Eating Habits

How many times did you hear growing up to chew your food? I always thought it was my parents just being difficult. I didn't think it mattered if my food was chewed or not because it was all going to the same place. Boy was I ever wrong. For years I had a habit of eating fast or grabbing something on the run and wolfing it down so fast I didn't even taste it. Because I ate so much and barely tasted my food, I often was still hungry and usually overate. Plus I was one of those people who needed to wash every swallow of my food down with something to drink (usually a soda). I always wound up with stomach pains and as embarrassing as it is to admit, some bad gas.

I never knew that if food is not chewed properly, it is not digested properly so not only was I not tasting my food, I was depriving myself of important nutrients in the food which was also contributing to me not feeling right all the time. I was always so stressed to get other things done that I never took the time-out to sit and really chew my food.

My advice is that when you eat, focus on the task at hand. Do not watch TV or read. Sit down at the table and leave when you are finished. Consciously eat slowly to give your stomach time to tell your brain when it's full. If you're still hungry after finishing your meal, wait 20 minutes before having a second helping or dessert.

The better you take care of yourself, the more likely you'll feel at your best!

Changes You Can Make

The changes you can make to your diet are simple. Even if you are not hypoglycemic, you still might benefit from making the same changes if you were hypoglycemic. Along with those changes you can also help reduce your anxiety by doing the following

• Eat more fresh and whole foods

• Eat more fresh fish and less red meat

• Increase your fiber intake

• Drink more water. Try to have at least 8 glasses of water a day

• Eat more vegetables.

• Make sure you eat balanced meals also.

• Chew your food!! Listen to your parents!

By making these changes to your diets, you will see a huge improvement in how you feel and how you handle stress.

Chapter 9 - Talking To Yourself

If you suffer from an anxiety disorder, you are familiar with self-talk. Usually in the midst of a panic attack or any high anxiety moment, you find your self being very negative. There are four types of self-talk that usually resemble a personality train that may be dominate in you.

Tip:

Become an expert at recognizing your own automatic negative thoughts. Break down each anxious thought until it is very specific. The less vague your thoughts are, the easier it is to challenge them and reduce your anxiety.

The Worrier

One of my favorite childhood authors Shel Silverstein wrote a poem in one of his books called "What if" and to this day it is my favorite poem. While some of the what if scenarios in his poems are a meant to be taken lightly (what if green hair grows on my chest) The rest of the poem is a classic example of a worrier trait. What if is the mantra for any worrier. Worries create anxiety by imaging the worst case scenario. If you fall into this category chances are you expect the worst, overestimate the odds of something bad happening and create images of failure. A typical self-talk for a worrier would be "Oh no my head is hurting. What if it is an aneurysm and no one can help me?"

The Self Critic

You are your own worse critic. That is what I have always been told. Everyone has some insecurity that causes them to criticize themselves. Perhaps they feel their arms are too jiggle or their feet are funny. A critic however takes this a step further.

If you are a critic, you are constantly judging yourself and your behavior. You feel like a failure because you are unable to handle your panic or anxiety disorder. The self-talk a critic usually takes part in is "what a disappointment you are, or you are stupid for feeling this way."

The Victim

This is the part of you that feels helpless about your condition. You feel like it is incurable and you will always be this way. This is one of the most dangerous traits because it can leave you hopeless. Recovery seems to be an unobtainable goal and this is usually what brings on depression. You will usually have thoughts like "I'll never be able to get control over this." and might even want to give up trying to get a handle on your attacks or disorder.

The Perfectionist

Is very similar to the critic but instead of putting yourself down, you are goading yourself to do better. A perfectionist creates its anxiety by constantly telling itself that you should be working harder, or you should have everything under control. You have to please everyone and be nice to everyone no matter what they do or say to you. You have thoughts like "I have to get this job, or I have to be there for them when they call"

So can you experience all four types of negative self-talk? Can you be the worrier, the critic, the victim and the perfections all at once. Yes you most certainly can. I was and some days I still find myself engaging in negative self-talk. When I started experiencing my anxiety I would always find myself saying "what if this is it? What if it is a heart attack?" as they grew more frequent I would find myself getting more depressed with each episode because I felt stupid for having those feelings and I thought I would never get a handle on it. I was pushing the man   I was meant to marry away from me by not getting a handle on my attacks. I'm also a perfectionist. I have a hard time saying no to anyone and usually take on more than I can handle. I was the type of person who would put everything aside for someone else. If I had to say no to someone I felt like they would be furious with me for doing it.

One of the most beneficial things I learned when researching ways to manage my panic and anxiety was positive self-talk. It took a while and it feels funny at first, but it is something you will have to work at but the results are fantastic.

The first thing you need to learn to do is counter your negative self-talk with something positive. You might have to write down and rehearse saying these statements over and over again so you will believe them. Basically you are reprogramming all of your negative thoughts into positive thoughts. As I said, this does take practice. Think about it though, it took us years to master our negative self-talk, and to undue all that will take some time and dedication. This was one of the hardest part of recovery for me. I have spent years from the time I was a teen engaging in negative self-talk. It was a habit that was hard for me to break.

One of the first things I learned to do to turn my negative into positive was to ask myself some questions. I wrote down on a piece of paper the following questions:

• Is this always true,

• Has this been true in the past, and

• What are the chances of this happening?

Here is how I began to apply it.

When I felt a panic attack coming on and I had my first what if thought, my conversation with myself when something like this.

Oh my God I think I'm having a heart attack...

- Is this always true - I've thought I was having a heart attack many times in the past and I never was.

- Has this been true in the past- No it never has been true

- What are the chances of it really happening- after all the tests I have had done, I know I am healthy and my chances are small.

Every single time I felt my heart starting to pound I would go into the bathroom (which was my safe place) and have this conversation with myself. I would repeat this conversation for as long as the panic attack lasted.

Another thing I learned was to write down my positive statements and look over them all the time.   I took situations that I knew might send me into a panic and wrote a positive statement about it.   For example, I was afraid of elevators and getting stuck in one. Every time I stepped foot in an elevator my first thought was "what if this gets stuck and I have a panic at-tack?" I wrote that thought down and countered it by saying "I am confident and calm getting on the elevator". It is important to avoid negative when writing positive statements which is why I didn't say "I will not panic getting on an elevator" The hardest thing for me was to believe in my statements. In fact some of the statements I originally wrote I had to change because I just didn't believe them. I had a journal full of negative statements that went through my mind everyday and I kept copies of these statements all over the place. I carried a copy in my bag at work so if I felt an attack coming on at work, I would grab my back and go look at my statements and repeat them out loud. As I progressed I found that I was able to change my statements into more positive statements because I believed it was working.

Another thing I learned how to do was rationalize while I was having the panic attacks. Again this took a long, long, very long time to master. Every time I thought I was having heart attack and the feeling lasted for a while, I would keep repeating to myself that if I was having a heart attack it would have happened already. Or if I was having a stroke, it would have happened already. These thoughts and words helped me keep a clear head about the attacks and helped me identify the attacks even more.

The hardest part of my battle was recognizing the signs that an anxiety attack was coming on. In the next Chapter I'll elaborate further on this.

Stress building Personality Test

Here's a short stress building personality test you might want to take inventory on your current stress state.

Are You a Perfectionist?

• Do you feel constant pressure to achieve?

• Do you feel you haven't done enough, no matter what you do?

• Are you hard on yourself when you find Out you're not perfect?

• Do you drive yourself co be the best in what you do, giving up every thing in the pursuit of perfection?

Are You a Control Freak?

• Do you feel the need to be in control of everything and everyone?

- Do you think lack of control is a sign of weakness?

- Do you run your life by lists?

- Are you reluctant to delegate to others?

Are You a People Pleaser?

- Do you need to have everyone like you?

- Do you feel upset if someone doesn't like you?

- Do you care more for others than you do for yourself?

- Do you hide your negative feelings so as not to displease others?

Do You Feel Incompetent?

- Do you feel that you have poor judgment?

- Do you feel you lack common sense?

- Do you feel like an impostor?

- Do you feel that you don't do as good a job as others?

If you answer yes to any of these questions, you could have a potential problem there. More than two yeses in anyone area indicates a real roadblock.

Chapter 10 - Coping with Attacks

Whether you suffer from panic attacks or anxiety attacks they are never fun and they can also be downright scary if you do not know what they are. This can be one of the most intensely uncomfortable feeling that you may ever experience and knowing that it can happen again without any warning can leave you feeling hopeless and helpless.

If you have panic attacks, it may help to comfort you that you are not alone! You're not even one in a million. In America, it is estimated that almost 5% of the population suffer from some form of anxiety disorder.

For some, it may be the occasional panic attack that only crop up in particular situations-like when having to speak in front of others, while, for other people, it can be so frequent and recurring that it inhibits them from leaving their home.

But there is hope. There are ways that you can learn to cope with the attacks. You might even be able to make the attacks so insignificant they will no longer be a bother to you. Some may not work for you, but others just might. It helps to know some of the most common coping techniques for dealing with panic attacks when they begin. Try them all and keep using the ones that work for you!

There are five changes you should could try to decrease the attack.

Make it a regular routine to practice deep relaxation (Chapter 10)

1. Do visualization exercises (Chapter 10)

2. Develop a regular exercise program (Chapter 11)

3. Cut down or out completely all stimulates from your diet (Chapter 8)

4. Learn to express your feelings and accept them (Chapter 6)

5. Turn Negative Self-talk into Positive. (Chapter 6)

Now all five of these will not work the same for every person. I never could get the hang of deep relaxation and while I managed to acknowledge my feelings, I still am learning each day on how to express them.

Deflate the Danger

A panic attack is a natural body reaction. When you have a panic attack or anxiety attack you are going through the same physiological flight reactions that you might in a life threatening situation. The number one difference is there is no immediate danger. So why do people suffer from attacks if there is no danger? That is the million dollar questions that right now no one has the answer too. Some people believe there is always a reason for the attack while others believe that it can be caused from a temporary physiological imbalance. The only thing anyone knows for sure is that most people who suffer from anxiety have usually be dealing with long-term stress or have recently had a significant loss in their life.

Now since there is no immediate or at least apparent danger, you invent danger to explain the feelings we are having. If you are having heart palpitations your thoughts are "I'm having a heart attack or I'm dying". When you can't breathe, you might be thinking "I'm suffocating". I used to have headaches and a numbing sensation when I had an attack and I used to think "I'm having a stroke". It is these thoughts that make the panic attack grow stronger. I like to think of a panic attack as a monster and those thoughts were the food that made it stronger. The more food you feed it the stronger it gets until it controls your life and this was the point I was getting to until I learned to remind myself of a few key things.

The first thing I had to learn was that a panic attack DOES NOT and CANNOT cause a heart attack or cardiac arrest. It is a scary feeling though when you have heart palpitations and the first thing that will cross anyone's mind is a heart attack. I had to realize the sensations caused by these attacks are different from a heart attack. For starters my heart was racing, and pounding and it came and went in waves. It was never constant for a long period of time. Each time my mind said "heart attack" the feeling got worse. I would get chest pains off and on in the upper left side of my chest and sometimes moving around would help make these go away. he chest pain never lasted long. I never had a heart attack, so I didn't know what it felt like. I also sometimes made the mistake of reading online about heart attacks symptoms and saying to myself "Yep that is what I have right now", which made me only worse. Finally after talking with my doctor he explained to me that with a true heart attack, there is continuous pain and pressure and even a crushing sensation in the center of your chest. I never experienced a crushing sensation in the center of the chest. Also with a heart attack some people report that these sensations might lessen if they rest and worsen if they move. I realized with a panic attack I felt worse when I tried to lay down and better when I was moving. Also during a heart attack, any abnormalities will be picked up by an EKG, and during a panic attack there are no abnormalities. It took three trips to the ER and a full work up from my doctor to show me that my heart was fine and that heart attacks in people with a healthy cardiovascular system were rare.

The next thing is that a panic attack will not cause you to stop breathing. It's not uncommon during an attack to feel like you are hyperventilating. This is partly because of the stress you might under. That stress can cause the muscles in your chest to tighten and make it feel like you are suffocating. You will not stop breathing however. Your brain, during a panic attack will force you to breath because of a natural instinct. This is why you might find yourself gasping for breath throughout your attack.

Lastly, you will not go crazy during a panic attack. The fact that you think you may be going crazy is enough proof that you are not. Crazy people rarely are aware that they are crazy. Also going crazy does not happen as fast as a panic attack does. A crazy behavior that come with mental illnesses such as schizophrenia develop over time. I never hallucinated or heard voices while I was having a panic attacks but yet I was still convinced I was going crazy. It was the feeling of not understanding what was going on with my body that made me feel as if I was going crazy.

The thing I had to remember was that while not everyone has an anxiety attack, most people may experience some of the symptoms that I did while I was having a panic attack. The difference is they did not look at those symptoms as anything dangerous. In fact a majority of people are able to identify these same symptoms as being signs that they are too stressed out.

So now that we know what the dangerous thoughts are how do we get rid of these thought? The first thing we need to do is recognize the signs of a panic attack. By just recognizing your tendency to believe that harmless symptoms are signs of danger is the first step. Once you are aware of these feelings and that they will cause you no harm, you will eventually stop having the thoughts of something dangerous or even fatal happening to you.

Next, write down alternative explanations of you symptoms. Think of how you feel when you are experiencing an attack and write down all your symptoms. Then look at them and think of other explanations for them. For example   automatically I thought heart palpitations = heart problems or attack. But once I started digging I realized that the heart palpitations can be caused by an outburst of adrenaline due to a potential situation. For example when my husband left me alone at night to go to work, my heart always started to pound as it got darker and later because in my mind there was a potential threat that something would happen to me. That is when my heart would start to pound and I would find myself not being able to breathe. If you find yourself getting dizzy or faint, this isn't' because you are going to faint, but because of the increase in your blood pressure once you start feeling anxious or a little panicky.

Lastly and do not fight your panic attack when you are going through it. Fighting it only make it worse and ignoring it is the worse thing you can do. To overcome or at least be able to manage your panic attacks you need to face the symptoms and accept what your body is doing. When you try to fight against a panic attack, your body tends to tense up and make you feel even worse.   Let your feelings go and allow your body to have the symptoms. You should already be able to recognize that you are experiencing a panic attack and you know all the alternative explanations for your symptoms. Think to yourself "Ok, here I go. I've been through this before and nothing bad has happened to me. This will pass, I'm just going to let my body do its thing and then move on. I've been through this before" and you will be amazed at how quickly your panic attack will pass as opposed to how long it seems to last when you are fighting it. This ties into the positive self talk we talked about earlier. It takes some time and practice to recognize the signs of a panic attack and talking yourself through it is not something that happens overnight. I was able to pick up really fast when I was starting to have a panic attack, but trying to talk myself through it was very hard for me. I would say "Ok.you have been through this before and you were ok" but then another part of me would say "But what if this time is different? What if this is the real deal this time?". It took me a long time to realize that I can't go through my life thinking "what

89

if?" I had to tell myself it was not the real deal last time and chances are it is not the real deal this time. It was a long battle for me. There were times when I felt like I would never be able to be able to manage my attacks and that I was destined to suffer from these for the rest of my life.

Another challenge is to find out what situations or circumstances can trigger your anxiety attacks. People who suffer from agoraphobia can identify a little easier their anxiety triggers. Some start when they have to drive over a bridge, or be in an enclosed space. Most of the time they will avoid those situations to avoid the panic attacks. Other people have spontaneous panic attacks that come out of the blue. I suffered from both. I knew what triggered my attacks from an agoraphobic point of few. However, the out of the blue attacks I suffered from also. If you find yourself suffering from what you think are out of the blue attacks there are some things you can do. First, keep track of their occurrences for at least two weeks. Keep an eye open for what was taking place right before the attack took place and what went on hours before it happened. Ask yourself these questions also:

1. Am I under stress?

2. Am I alone or with someone? If you are with someone ask yourself if they are a friend, family or a stranger

3. How have I been feeling all day? What was my mood throughout the day?

4. Was I having any negative thoughts?

5. Am I tired?

6. Did I have a lot of caffeine right before everything happened?

These will help you identify a pattern to your attacks and what might trigger them. In my case, I noticed it I had a particularly trying day or had heard bad news, or became too overwhelmed with what I thought was everyday responsibilities I tend to have an attack usually that night. I also noticed that if I was alone, I was more prone to any attacks. Perhaps my biggest trigger was when I thought about my father who had passed away suddenly two years ago. By not dealing with his death, and keeping my emotions inside, I somehow convinced myself that I was going to die just as he did. Alone and from a heart attack.

I was taught some key coping strategies to add to what I had already learned. One of them was to talk to another person when I felt the symptoms coming on. Mainly to me that person was usually my husband. Sometimes if I felt the attack starting I would simply tell him to tell me a story or to start talking about something, anything to take my mind off it. Sometimes I would do the talking and tell him how I was feeling and what was going through my head. For times he wasn't around and I felt an attack starting I would talk to whoever was around me. I started up random conversations with people in the elevator to get my thoughts off it stopping and me being trapped. I never told these people of my fears but just saying something as simple as "Its beautiful outside isn't it" got my mind off my racing thought.

Another strategy that helped me out was to practice what some people call thought stopping. As soon as I felt the what if self talking in my head I would tell myself to stop or cut it out. If I was alone, I said these out loud and said it loudly. If I was around other people, I pictured the word stop. I would have to take a few deep breaths and constantly remind myself to stop the way I'm thinking.

Deep Relaxation

An important step to overcoming panic attacks is to relax. That's easy to say but difficult to do. A good way to do this is to concentrate on your breathing making sure it is slow and steady. One of the first signs of a panic attack is difficulty breathing, and you may find yourself panting to catch a breath. When you focus on making those breaths even, your heart rate will slow down and the panic will subside.

Breathing more slowly and deeply has a calming effect. A good way to breathe easier is to let all the air out of your lungs. This forces your lungs to reach for a deeper breath next time. Continue to focus on your out-breath, letting all the air out of your lungs and soon you'll find your breathing is deeper and you feel calmer.

Ideally, you want to take the focus off the fact that you are having a panic attack. Try to press your feet, one at a time, into the ground. Feel how connected and rooted they are to the ground.

An even better way is to lie down with your bottom near a wall. Place your feet against the wall (your knees are bent) and press your feet one at a time into the wall. If you can breathe in as you press your foot against the wall, and breathe out as you release it, it will be more effective. You should alternate between your feet. Do this for 10 - 15 minutes or until the panic subsides.

Use all of your senses to take full notice of what you see, hear, feel, and smell in your environment. This will help you to remain present. Panic is generally associated with remembering upsetting events from the past or expecting something upsetting in the future. Anything that helps keep you focused in the present will be calming. Try holding a pet; looking around your room and noticing the colors, textures, and shapes; listening closely to the sounds you hear; call a friend; or smell the smells that are near you.

Many people strongly support aromatherapy to deal with panic and anxiety. Lavender can have an especially calming and soothing effect when you smell it. You can find essential oil of lavender at many stores. Keep it handy and take a sniff when you start feeling anxious.

Try putting a few drops of lavender essence oil into some oil (olive or grape seed oil will do) and rub on your body. Keep a prepared mixture in a dark glass bottle for when you need it. You can even prepare several bottles, with a small one to carry with you.

Other essential oils known to help panic and panic attacks are helichrysum, frankincense, and marjoram. Smell each of them, and use what smells best to you, or a combination of your favorite oils mixed in olive or grape seed oil.

Another great tool to combating anxiety and stress is to use visualization.

Visualization

The purpose of visualization is to enable you to quickly clear mental stress, tension, and anxious thinking. The visualization can be used when feeling stressed and is useful when your mind is racing with fearful, anxious thinking.

This visualization process, when practiced often, is effective for removing deep-seated mental anxieties or intrusive thoughts. To gain maximum benefit, the exercise must be carried out for longer then 10 minutes at a time, as anything shorter will not bring noticeable results.

There is no right or wrong way to carry out the visualization. Be intuitive with it and do not feel you are unable to carry it out if you feel you are not very good at seeing mental imagery. As long as your attention is on the exercise, you will gain benefit.

It is best to do this exercise in a quiet place where you won't be disturbed, and then when you are more practiced you will be able to get the same positive results in a busier environment such as the workplace. You should notice a calming effect on your state of mind along with a sensation of mental release and relaxation.

Either sitting or standing, close your eyes and move your attention to your breath. To become aware of your breathing, place one hand on your upper chest and one on your stomach. Take a breath and let your stomach swell forward as you breathe in and fall back gently as you breathe out. Take the same depth of breath each time and try to get a steady rhythm going.

Your hand on your chest should have little or no movement. Again, try to take the same depth of breath each time you breathe in. This is called Diaphragmatic Breathing.

When you feel comfortable with this technique, try to slow your breathing rate down by creating a short pause after you have breathed out and before you breathe in again. Initially, it may feel as though you are not getting enough air in, but with regular practice this slower rate will soon start to feel comfortable.

It is often helpful to develop a cycle where you count to three when you breathe in, pause, and then count to three when you breathe out (or 2, or 4--whatever is comfortable for you). This will also help you focus on your breathing without any other thoughts coming into your mind.

94

If you are aware of other thoughts entering your mind, just let them go and bring your attention back to counting and breathing. Continue doing this for a few minutes. (If you practice this, you will begin to strengthen the Diaphragmatic Muscle, and it will start to work normally leaving you with a relaxed feeling all the time.)

Now move your attention to your feet. Try to really feel your feet. See if you can feel each toe. Picture the base of your feet and visualize roots growing slowly out through your soles and down into the earth. The roots are growing with quickening pace and are reaching deep into the soil of the earth. You are now rooted firmly to the earth and feel stable like a large oak or redwood tree.

Stay with this feeling of grounded safety and security for a few moments. Once you have created a strong feeling or impression of being grounded like a tree, visualize a cloud of bright light forming way above you. A bolt of lightning from the luminous cloud hits the crown of your head, and that ignites a band of bright white light descending slowly from your head all the way down your body, over your legs, and out past your toes.

As the band of light passes over you, feel it clearing your mental state. It is illuminating your mind and clearing any disturbing or stressful thoughts that you may have been thinking about. Repeat this image four or five times until you feel a sense of clearing and release from any anxious thinking.

In finishing, see yourself standing under a large, luminescent waterfall. The water is radiant and bubbling with vitality and life. As you stand under the waterfall, you can feel the water run over every inch of your body, soothing you and instilling within you a sense of deep calm.

Try to taste the water. Open your mouth and let it run into your mouth, refreshing you. Hear it as it bounces off the ground around you. The water is life itself and it is washing away stress and worry from your mind and body. After a moment, open your eyes.

Try to use all of your senses when carrying out the visualization. To make the pictures in your mind as real as possible, use your senses of touch, taste, and hearing. Feel the water trickle down your body; hear the sound it makes as it splashes over you.

The more realistic the imagined scenarios, the more benefit you will gain. Many people report useful and soothing results from using these simple visualizations often. The mind is much like a muscle in that, in order to relax, it needs to regularly release what it is holding onto.

You can use any situation or location that will help calm you. We liken this to "finding your happy place". Maybe you feel relaxed in a swimming pool or on the beach. Imagine yourself there. Just make sure wherever you go in your mind is a place where you can be calm and rested.

By visualizing the different situations, you are allowing your mind to release. It is like sending a message to your brain that when you close your eyes and begin this process it is time for letting go of anything that it has been mentally holding onto, including anxious thinking.

To train your mind how to let go of the stress, it is important to practice this daily. With practice, you can learn to release all stress within minutes of starting the exercise. Your daily practice should take place before going to bed, as that will enable you to sleep more soundly.

Many people do not do these visualizations in the bed-room but some other room before going to bed. That way, when they enter the bedroom and close the door, they are leaving the mental stress and anxious thinking behind them. Just be sure you have the opportunity to concentrate on your mental images.

Visualization as a tool for dealing with mental stress is very effective. If such visualization is carried out properly, you can reach a deep feeling of inner calm. This technique probably will not work in helping to end an anxiety attack, but it can help that attack from beginning. It is a powerful support tool for rid-ding yourself of general anxiety sensations.

With practice, you find you go days without having anx-ious thinking interrupt your life, and importantly, this signifi-cantly reduces the level of general anxiety you feel.

Visualization is simply a tool you can use to overcome anxious thoughts and feelings.

Managing your attacks does not happen overnight. In fact it took me at least six months to fully get this all down pat and another six months before I had it all perfected. I took baby steps and first learned to tell the signs of a panic attack. Once I had that down, I tackled my negative thoughts and I said I had battles with myself because I was so negative. It did not take me a year to start feeling better though. I started feeling better once I was able to identify the signs of an attack. I also learned how to manage my stress and one of the most helpful things was an ex-ercise program.

Chapter 11 - Exercise, Exercise, Exercise...

This is one of the most effective methods for reducing stress and anxiety. There are many benefits to a good exercise program

- Production of endorphins which increase your sense of well-being

- Improved circulation

- Improved digestion

- A rapid metabolism of excess adrenaline in the bloodstream

- Helps reduce problems sleeping

- Can reduce depression

- Can reduce stress and anxiety also

One of the biggest problems most people face today is having no outlet for their stress. Usually you might wind up taking it out your stress on people who are close to you. While there are other things you can do such as beating a pillow, exercise however seems to be the number one solution to reducing your stress.

Caution:

If you're over 35 or in poor physical condition, don't start an exercise program before you see a doctor for a physical exam and a treadmill test.

Before you even start an exercise program you have to assess your fitness level so you know what program to choose. See if you have any symptoms of being out of shape. Some of them are being out of breath every time you walk up a flight of stairs and you have a hard time catching your breath from it. Does basic exercise exhaust you? Also look at how active you are. How often do you work out and how long? If the answer is hardly ever, you will probably benefit from an exercise program!

Now I know you are excited, but are you really ready for an exercise program? If you have never had an exercise routine before, you want to meet with your doctor to make sure you have no underlying factors that could be aggravated with exercise. You should especially see your doctor for a physical if you are over 40 and not used to much exercise.

Choosing An Exercise program

There are so many programs out there, that everyone should be able to find a program they can do and stick with. Most of the time you should look at what you want to get from exercise to help decide what program to stick with

Aerobic exercise is great for reducing generalized anxiety and panic attacks. This exercise requires the use of you larger muscles and is great for cardiovascular condition which is the capacity of your circulatory system to deliver oxygen to your tissue and cells. A good aerobic exercise program can consist of any of the following; running, walking, cycling either outdoors or on a stationary bike, swimming, dancing and kickboxing.

You can also look into a good strength training program to gain muscle strength. Strength training can help tone your muscles and give you a leaner look. If you want to socialize and meet people then you should try to engage in a cardio workout like racquetball. You can even take up golfing though it is not a cardio workout, it is a great stress reliever. The week before our wedding, I and my husband spent the afternoon at a golfing range just to get all the stress from the wedding off our chests. It was the best day out we had in a long time.

Tip:

Too much exercise all at once will simply pile on more stress than you need. Start slowly, and gradually increase the length and difficulty of your exercise

Another good idea to think about is if you want your exercise program to be outside. Sometimes just the fresh air can help clear your head and give you a better sense of perception. You can do running, walking, biking, hiking and even gardening outside.

For me, I needed an aerobic workout that was going to be an outlet of my stress and help me sleep at night. My best friend had recommended kickboxing and I was hooked after my first class. Being able to punch and kick at imaginary people was just what I needed to get my pent up stress out, though I would recommend if you are new to exercise, you take it slow if you go the kickboxing route.

Besides kickboxing, I am a big walker. I love to walk, whether it is walking around outside on a beautiful day or doing laps around my local mall. Walking is the most highly recommended exercise for not only managing stress but also for losing weight. It is easy to do and does not require any special equipment and the risk of hurting yourself is slim.

Getting Your Program Started.

So now that you have an idea on what you want to do, how should you start. Assuming you have never exercised before you have to start slow. If you start off to hard-and-fast from the beginning you are going to burn yourself out. Here are some guidelines if you have never exercised before

Start off slowly. Most doctors will tell you that if you never exercised before you should start off exercising for 10 minutes or until you feel winded every other day for at least the first week. Then with each passing week, add 5 more minutes to your routine until you reach about 30 minutes. You should also give it a trial of one month. Most people who have never exercised before will experience some discomfort those first few weeks. You may feel achy and sore and find yourself having a hard time pushing yourself to do the exercise. However most people say that after the first month is when they start to experience enough benefits to motivate them to keep going.

Speaking of achy and sore, expect this! The saying goes "No pain, no gain". The soreness you may be feelings is a sign that you are doing it right and stretching your body the way it needs to be. Making it a habit to warm up before you begin will help reduce some of the soreness you will feel the next day. After a vigorous workout, make sure you give yourself a cool down. If you are working out on a machine in the gym, you will see that most machines such as the elliptical and treadmill will automatically factor in a five-minute cool down where they will lessen the intensity. Even if you are not on a machine, you should still remember to do a cool down. If you were jogging, spend a few minutes when you are done walking around to bring the blood back from your muscles to the rest of your body.

While some people use exercise to help them sleep at night, it is not a good idea to exercise less than two hours before you go to sleep. Your endorphins have been kicked into overdrive and you may find yourself to wound up to sleep. Most people enjoy working out first thing in the morning to get their energy up for the day.

Using Exercise To Help Reduce Anxiety

When you are using exercise to reduce anxiety, keep these points in mind. Your exercise should be ideally aerobic and you should aim for doing your exercise 20-30 minutes at least 4-5 times a week. Aim to hit your target heart rate for at least 10 minutes during your routine. How do you figure out your target heart rate this is the formula to use (220-your age)x.75 for you can use the following chart

Age	Heart Rate
20-29	145-164
30-39	138-156
40-49	130-148
50-59	122-140
60-69	116-132

Lastly, avoid exercising only one time a week. When you do spurts of exercising you are adding more stress to your body and it is doing more harm than good. However say you can only make it to the gym once that week, you should walk for the rest of the week.

Overcoming Excuses For Not Exercising

Exercise, we all have excuses for avoiding them. I am guilty of it myself. Some of the most common excuses I have are I don't have the time, I'm too tired, Exercising is boring, It's a pain to have to go somewhere to exercise, and what if I have a panic attack while I'm exercising.

I don't have the time to exercise is the number one excuse most people use when it comes to exercise. I've even used this one several times. I thought there was no way possible I could take 30 minutes out of my busy day to exercise. I felt there were more important things to do then to exercise. The reason why I had no time to exercise was because I never was willing to make the time. There were so many little changes I could have made to give me the time. Instead of spending 20 minutes in the morning picking out my outfit for the day and ironing it, I could do it the night before instead and use those 20 minutes to workout. Instead of coming home on my lunch hour and sitting and watching TV, I could walk around my building for a half hour. It wasn't until I realized how important exercise was to managing my attacks that I began to make these changes.

I'm too tired to exercise. This is another one of my favorites and more common if you are going to exercise at the end of the day. How many times have you skipped the gym because you were to tired at the end of the day. It is just as easy though to say in the morning you are too tired to get up and exercise. What you might not know is that exercise can overcome tiredness and that if you exercise regardless of how tired you feel, you will find yourself feeling reenergized afterwards!

Exercise is boring. There are some people out there than can get bored doing the same activity over and over again, which is why they are given a number of options on what exercise to do. Maybe the one exercise you have been doing is boring so have you tried others? How about trying a work out buddy? I think one of the reasons why I enjoyed kickboxing so much was because I did it with a friend. I even liked going to the gym more if I went with someone. If no one is around, try switching up your routine. Some days walk, other days pop in a video and do that. There are some fantastic exercise videos out there. With all the options there are out there for a good exercise routine, you should never find yourself bored.

It's a pain to have to go somewhere to exercise. You do not have to belong to a gym to get a good workout. I said before there are hundreds of exercise videos out on the market today. You can do everything from kickboxing to walking in the comfort of your own home. There is also a great demand for exercise equipment. Think about buying a bike, or a treadmill to use. If you think you might get bored from that, place the exercise machine in front of the TV and work out to that. Or keep a radio nearby. We had an exercise machine and I would plop in a DVD and watch that while I worked out. I would get so caught up in what I was watching that the 30 minutes flew by. If you don't want to spend the money on exercise equipments or videos, just turn on your radio and dance your heart out for a good 20 minutes or so!

What if I have a panic attack? Jumping into a tough program when you have never exercised before might well create the same symptoms of a panic attack, but a nice brisk walk will not. If you start to feel uneasy or you are losing control, stop and wait until you compose yourself before continuing. Talk to yourself and realize that you are not having a panic attack out of the blue, it is just your body's normal response to the exercise you are not use to.

Exercise is an important part of recovery and managing your anxiety. The benefits of exercise is not only going to help you manage your anxiety and your stress better, but the other health benefits far outweigh any excuse you may have to get out of it.

Chapter 12 - Use the Tools You Have

No one expects you to wake up one morning and discover you are "cured" of your panic attacks. You should however try to carry out some of the ideas mentioned here, especially if you do not want to take any medication.

Anxiety is not something to be ashamed of. It is a problem that affects more people than you might realize. I always thought I was the only person who was going through it, and now I am finding all sorts of people who suffer from anxiety in one form or another. Some of them are on medication and some of them took the same route I did to manage their attacks.

It's been nearly 3 years since I started having panic attacks. I am nowhere near cured, as my last panic attack was back in May, but I was able to identify it and deal with it so quick that it did not even affect me. If I can learn to manage my panic attacks and anxiety, then so can you.

Now take that important first step.....

Riverside, CA, January 2008

Reference

External links

Anxiety Disorders Association of America. Information for families, clinicians and researchers

http://www.adaa.org/

National Institute of Anxiety and Stress. Information and treatment options for individuals

http://www.conqueranxiety.com/

Anxietyshare. Share events you are anxious about with others and get advice and support.

http://www.anxietyshare.com/

Further reading

Bourne, J. Edmund (2005), The Anxiety & Phobia Workbook, New Harbinger Publications, Inc. Oakland, ISBN 1-57224-413-5

Buell, Linda Manassee (2001),Panic and Anxiety Disorder 121 Tips, Real -Life Advice, Resources & More, Simplify Life, Poway ISBN 1-926507-04-7

Carbonell, David Ph.D (2004) Panic Attacks Workbook. A Guided program For Beating the Panic Trick Ulysses Press, Berkeley ISBN 1-56975-415-2

Frish, Noreen Cavan, Frish, Lawrence E. (1998) Psychiatric Mental Health Nursing, Delmar Publishers, Albany ISBN 0-8273-7233-7

Turkington, Carol A. (1998) Stress Management for Busy people. McGraw-Hill, New york. ISBN 0-07-065535-9

Vanin, John & Helsley, James (2007), Anxiety Disorders: A Pocket Guide For Primary Care, Humana Press, ISBN 978-1-58829-923-9

Printed in the United States
146453LV00010B/228/A